To Moira
From your Hill Country Pals.
♡ Kelly, Erin & Bob

ARMADILLOS
to
ZIZIPHUS

The Corrie Herring Hooks Series

ARMADILLOS
to
ZIZIPHUS

A Naturalist in the Texas Hill Country

David M. Hillis
Foreword by Harry W. Greene

University of Texas Press

Austin

Versions of some chapters in this book originally appeared in a column titled "Mason County Science Corner" in the *Mason County News*, 2020–2021.

Unless otherwise indicated, all photos are by the author.

Requests for permission to reproduce material from this work should be sent to:
    Permissions
    University of Texas Press
    P.O. Box 7819
    Austin, TX 78713-7819
    utpress.utexas.edu/rp-form

♾ The paper used in this book meets the minimum requirements of ANSI/NISO Z39.48-1992 (R1997) (Permanence of Paper).

Library of Congress Cataloging-in-Publication Data

Names: Hillis, David M., 1958– author. | Greene, Harry W., 1945– writer of
    foreword.
Title: Armadillos to Ziziphus : a naturalist in the Texas Hill Country / David M.
    Hillis.
Description: First edition. | Austin : University of Texas at Austin, 2023. | Includes
    index.
Identifiers: LCCN 2022013440
    ISBN 978-1-4773-2673-2 (cloth)
    ISBN 978-1-4773-2674-9 (PDF)
    ISBN 978-1-4773-2675-6 (ePub)
Subjects: LCSH: Biodiversity—Texas—Texas Hill Country. | Biotic communities—
    Texas—Texas Hill Country. | Endemic plants—Texas—Texas Hill Country. |
    Animals—Texas—Texas Hill Country. | Climatic changes—Texas—Texas Hill
    Country.
Classification: LCC QH105.T49 H55 2023 | DDC 577.09764—dc23/
    eng/20220331
LC record available at https://lccn.loc.gov/2022013440

doi:10.7560/326732

Contents

Foreword by Harry W. Greene *ix*
Preface *xiii*

I. THE TEXAS HILL COUNTRY: A NATURALIST'S
PARADISE *1*

1. Geological Setting of the Edwards Plateau *7*
2. From Acid Sands to Alkaline Clays *16*
3. Hill Country Weather: Droughts, Floods, and Severe
   Storms *20*
4. Some Texas Icons Haven't Been Here All That Long *26*
5. Hill Country Endemics *30*
6. What Is the Value of Biodiversity? *34*

II. THE SEASONAL LIFE OF A VERNAL POOL *41*

7. Tilting at Tiny Windmills *43*
8. Crustacean Wonders *47*
9. The Fascinating Flora of Vernal Pools *50*
10. Those Who Live in Glass Houses *55*
11. A Season of Symphonies *58*
12. What Happened to All Our Frogs? *63*

III. FLOWING WATERS: AQUIFERS, CAVES,
SPRINGS, AND RIVERS *69*

13. Life without Light *73*
14. Lanterns of Summer *77*
15. Musings about Mussels *81*
16. The Last Wild River *84*

IV. LIFE OF A GRASSLAND 91

17. Why Do Some Grasses Grow in the Winter, but Others in the Summer? 93
18. Butterflies, Hummingbirds, and Other Pollinators 97
19. The Noble Life of a Dung-Roller 101
20. Where Have All the Quail Gone? 106
21. Grasshoppers, Locusts, and Plagues 110
22. The History of Texas Cattle Written in Their DNA 115

V. IN THE WOODLANDS AND BRUSHLANDS 121

23. Containing and Preventing Oak Wilt 123
24. The Challenges of Being an Oak Tree in the Hill Country 127
25. How Do Trees Sense When It Is Time to Leaf Out and Bloom? 131
26. The Dr. Jekyll and Mr. Hyde of Trees 135
27. Spring Is Here, and So Are the Snakes 139
28. Songs of the Summer Dog Days 143
29. Going Batty 147
30. Deer Densities on the Edwards Plateau 151
31. Bucks in Velvet 155
32. The Future of Hill Country Deer Populations 159
33. The Carbon Cycle and How It Affects Our Daily Lives 163

VI. BACKYARD BIOLOGY 169

34. The Remarkable Life of Hummingbirds 171
35. Ways to Attract and Increase Bird Populations 175
36. The Unexpected Beauty and Diversity of Lichens 179
37. There Is More to Mistletoe Than Kissing 183
38. The Ups and Downs of Ants 186
39. A Pattern in the Web 190

40. Caterpillar Plagues and Their Connection to the Weather *193*

41. Predators and Second Chances *197*

VII. CLIMATIC ADAPTATIONS *203*

42. Toadally Cool *205*

43. The Surprising Life Cycle of a Monarch Butterfly *207*

44. How Do Animals Survive the Winter? Part 1: Migrating *211*

45. How Do Animals Survive the Winter? Part 2: Keeping Warm and Active *215*

46. How Do Animals (and Plants) Survive the Winter? Part 3: Waiting Out the Cold *219*

VIII. RESTORATION AND THE FUTURE OF THE HILL COUNTRY'S NATURAL RESOURCES *225*

47. The Restoration and Benefits of Native Grasses *229*

48. The Pros and Cons of Brush Control *233*

49. Recovery of a Texas Icon: The Texas Horned Lizard *237*

50. Avoiding the Dangers of Lead Poisoning in Game Meat *240*

51. Our Climate Future in Central Texas *244*

52. If the Earth Is Warming, Why Did We Have a Record Cold Snap? *248*

53. Practical, Painless, and Significant Solutions to Climate Change *252*

54. Six Resolutions for Supporting Native Plants and Animals *256*

Index *261*

Foreword

Mid-nineteenth-century military surveyors, traveling northwestward from coastal Texas, wrote of abruptly extensive uplands, covered in a rich mosaic of savanna-woodlands and dissected by countless streams as well as several large rivers. Having several hundred miles later surmounted a second more open tableland, the Llano Estacado, those early explorers then referred to as First Plateau what geologists decades later officially named the Edwards Plateau. Today that ecoregion encompasses all or parts of 41 out of 254 Texas counties, about 15 percent of the state's overall area. Its eastern, southern, and southwestern boundaries are sharply demarcated by the Balcones Escarpment, which is straddled by Austin, San Antonio, and several smaller cities. The northern border of what most folks refer to simply as the Hill Country is more gradual and passes through roughly the geographical center of Texas, between the towns of Brady and Brownwood.

The Hill Country's ecological significance and beauty are far beyond what would be expected based on its areal coverage or topography. Using the lingo of science, I note that these 36,680 square miles—slightly larger than Indiana—make up a continental-scale ecotone, a place where two significantly different habitats merge to some extent over a relatively small distance. In this case, moist, sometimes forested Gulf coastal prairies abut the drier southern Great Plains along the Balcones Escarpment. Thus, in comparison with most other similarly sized chunks of North America, the Hill Country harbors exceptionally high biological diversity. Put differently, this natural wealth—thanks to its central location on a south to north gradient of decreasing temperature and an east to west gradient of decreasing rainfall—is such that a relatively mild climate plays out over arid mesas, humid canyonlands, and extremely complex geology and hydrology. In the Hill Country, a few hundred acres of well-managed ranchland can be home to about 35 species of native mammals, 50 species of amphibians and reptiles, and nearly 100 species of birds. Lovers of the outdoors will find, within a few feet of each other, dry-adapted Claret Cup Cacti and moisture-loving Cliff-brake Ferns. With luck, one might treasure encounters with Copperheads, whose species range extends from here to the Carolinas, and Western Diamond-backed Rattlesnakes, found all the way to southern California.

The Hill Country is rightfully famous among Texas residents and tourists from all over the world, and several earlier books have addressed various aspects of its natural and cultural history. *Armadillos to Ziziphus: A Naturalist in the Texas Hill Country* is unique, however, because David Hillis is, first, a world-renowned biologist and educator, able to deliver authoritative coverage from the standpoint of firsthand scholarship. As it happens, he also is an insatiably curious person who has done decades of research and manual labor in a variety of landscapes. David's peripatetic youth included being born in Denmark, living in several other countries, and undertaking a formative early childhood visit to the Hill Country. After graduating from Baylor University, he received graduate degrees from the University of Kansas, taught briefly at the University of Miami, and since 1987 has been a distinguished professor at the University of Texas at Austin. David's numerous honors include a MacArthur Fellowship (informally known as a "genius award") and election to the National Academy of Sciences. He has mentored thousands of undergraduates and many dozens of Ph.D. students, all the while serving on the boards of The Nature Conservancy in Texas and other civic groups. In addition to hundreds of scientific journal papers, he wrote a pioneering volume on using molecular biology to understand evolutionary relationships among organisms and has authored two widely adopted introductory biology texts. Beginning in 1996, much of David's spare time has been devoted to raising Longhorns, restoring native grasses, planting food crops, hunting, and fine-tuning energy and water conservation on his Double Helix Ranch in Mason County.

Armadillos to Ziziphus is neither a technical treatise nor a guidebook in any traditional sense. Professor Hillis writes like he speaks, prone to neither unnecessary jargon nor talking down to his audience. His evocative but easy-going style makes reading this book like taking an extended journey with a gifted teacher and friend, at a pace of one's own choosing. Be forewarned by the table of contents, however; the breadth of topics covered here is downright astonishing. Some of the time it's as if we're in a vehicle, slowly traveling backroads to popular destinations like Hamilton Pool, Lost Maples State Natural Area, and The Nature Conservancy's James River Bat Cave. Other times we're hurtling by canoe down a remote boulder-strewn river stretch, marveling over the power of sudden storms and pausing to appreciate the rock shelter art of Archaic Pecos people. More often it's as if we're out for a walk with David on his ranch, pausing to view through a hand lens the freshwater Fairy Shrimp in a vernal pool or scope out the floral structures of pasture forbs. We learn how hail forms and about the crazy little wheel animacules called rotifers; we get advice on everything from why and how to coexist with dung beetles to protecting fruit orchards from unusual freezing events. All along the way readers will painlessly learn a lot of biology—like how trees know when to be dormant and why a population explosion of raccoons has been so rough on ground-nesting birds, frogs, and lizards.

This is a book for study and learning, for the pleasures of reading, and, if you're so inclined, for meditation on the joys and lessons that come from nature study. We live in daunting, perilous times, so *Armadillos to Ziziphus* also addresses the near-term horrors of the viral COVID pandemic and the longer-term catastrophes arising from global climate change that threaten us all. David Hillis ends this inspiring volume with hopeful, practical suggestions for how we can as individuals and responsible members of society strive for a better future, out in our beloved Hill Country and beyond.

Harry W. Greene is the author of *Snakes: The Evolution of Mystery in Nature* and *Tracks and Shadows: Field Biology as Art.*

Preface

There are some who can live without wild things,
and some who cannot. These essays are the delights
and dilemmas of one who cannot.

Aldo Leopold, from the foreword to *A Sand
County Almanac*

I have long wanted to write a book about the natural history of the
Texas Hill Country. There are plenty of field guides for identifying the native plants and animals of the area, as well as guides to
parks and natural areas. This book fills a different need; it contains
essays about how biodiversity and natural history connect to our
enjoyment of and appreciation of life. It explores ways in which we
might better understand, preserve, and restore the natural beauty
and diversity of the Hill Country. I wrote this book for landowners,
visitors, residents, sportspeople, nature lovers, and other outdoor
enthusiasts who wish to explore and experience the Hill Country with a deeper sense of understanding of its natural beauty. The
more we understand and experience nature, the more of it we will
appreciate, and the more we will seek to protect it for future generations to enjoy.

When I was a college undergraduate, I worked on a research
project on the reproductive lives of leopard frogs. One day, I was
plotting out the locations of my study sites on a map of Texas, when
an older classmate peered over my shoulder to see what I was working on. He knew that I had recently moved to Texas from "back
east," and he wanted to be sure that I understood the importance of
the map before us. He traced the Edwards Plateau with his finger,
looked at me, and said solemnly, "This is God's country." He then
pointed to the headwaters of the South Llano River and said, with

a twinkle in his eye, "and He lives right there." The conviction in his voice suggested to me that I should not argue the point. To many who live or visit there, the Texas Hill Country is a special place, to be treated with a certain reverence.

I learned a lot in my classes as an undergraduate, but I devoted a lot more time in college to exploring the Texas Hill Country, learning everything I could about the interesting plants and animals that live there. Since then, although I have lived parts of my life on all the world's inhabited continents, the Texas Hill Country has always felt like home to me. When my wife, Ann, and I had a chance to move back here early in my academic career, we did not hesitate to do so. Since then, despite offers to live and work in other places, we've never been tempted enough to leave. Now, as director of the University of Texas Biodiversity Center, I get to study, teach, write, and talk to the public about the spectacular diversity of life. It is hard to do that from a better place than the Texas Hill Country.

I've written this book from a personal viewpoint, largely based on my research into the diversity of life as a professor at the University of Texas at Austin. Many of the chapters explore and explain research projects and subjects that I've worked on, in a manner that I hope will be of interest to a broad audience, and in a way that relates to common experiences one might have walking around in the Hill Country. My goal is that this book will help people understand and appreciate what they see when they live, play, and visit in the area.

A brief note about the treatment of species names: When common names clearly apply to a specific species, I have treated them as proper names and capitalized them throughout the book. Generic or informal names that apply to multiple species (such as rattlesnake, deer, or quail) are not capitalized, whereas formal names that identify particular species (such as Western Diamond-backed Rattlesnake, Whitetail, or Bobwhite) are capitalized. This has long been the accepted style for some groups (including birds, amphibians, and reptiles), so I've extended this style to all species for consistency.

During my career, Ann and I have purchased ranches in Blanco and Mason Counties in the Hill Country and worked to restore their natural beauty. Our sons, Erec and Jonathan, have grown up on these properties, and now the Hill Country is as much a part of their lives as it is of ours. I hope that they will continue to love, enjoy, appreciate, and protect our ranches for their children, and for their children's children, and that this book will help instill the love and understanding of the land that is necessary for that to happen.

Several people have given me extensive and helpful feedback on the essays in this book. In particular, Harry W. Greene, Ann Hillis, John Karges, and Greg Pauly read the entire manuscript and made many useful suggestions. I also received comments and input on individual chapters from Larry Gilbert, Tom Givnish, Nancy Greig, Tony Plutino, Richard Tracy, and Hal Zesch. I am grateful to Chris Barnhart, Bill J. Boyd, Kenny Braun, Reagan Edwards, Larry Gilbert, Bruce W. Leander, Melody Lytle, Tahmineh Rouzbahani, Edward Theriot, Alex Wild, Ian M. Wright, and Amy Zesch for use of their photographs. Nicole Elmer prepared the map of the Texas Hill Country. My editors at the University of Texas Press—Casey Kittrell, Lynne Ferguson, and Lorraine Atherton—had many useful suggestions for making this book accessible to a wide audience. I thank Linda Ronan for her work on book design, Cameron Ludwick for book publicity, Christina Vargas for assisting with many aspects of the book's production, and the rest of the talented team at UT Press who helped make this book possible.

Finally, I thank all my colleagues, friends, and family who have accompanied me on countless field trips across the Texas Hill Country. A bad day in the field beats a great day in the office anytime.

ARMADILLOS
to
ZIZIPHUS

I

THE TEXAS HILL COUNTRY

A Naturalist's Paradise

My first memories of the Texas Hill Country—more formally the Edwards Plateau and associated geological regions—date to a fishing trip I took as a very young child, along with my father, brother, and a family friend. My father, a physician with the Air Force at the time, was stationed in San Antonio. He was a viral epidemiologist, and his work on tropical diseases would later take our family to diverse places all over the globe—wherever there were emerging viral epidemics. But my first real connection to the wonders of the Earth's biodiversity came on that Hill Country fishing trip.

◄ The Edwards Plateau in bloom. The spring wildflower displays of the Texas Hill Country are legendary, drawing many visitors to the region every year. These are in Mason County.

Although I was excited about seeing and catching fish, it was all the spectacular plants and other animals of the Hill Country that truly caught my eye. Not far outside of San Antonio, we spotted a mother skunk, followed by her tiny offspring. My dad stopped the car to let the skunk cross the road, and we all marveled as her mirror-image kits struggled to climb the roadside embankment as they followed their mom. I don't know if it was their beauty, the commonalities of the interactions of a parent with her offspring, or just the comical nature of the baby skunk movements that captured my imagination and attention. In any case, although that encounter with skunks was some six decades ago, that moment is still seared into my memory. I had no idea how it would happen at the time, but I knew then that somehow, my life was going to be focused on discovering and experiencing the spectacular diversity of life.

After San Antonio, my father's job carried our family to various parts of tropical Africa and Asia, where I pursued butterflies; watched birds; went fishing; caught lizards, snakes, and frogs; and generally spent every waking moment that I could in the woods, on the water, or in the fields. My parents sometimes worried that I was too distracted by the wonders of the natural world, and more than once my father wondered aloud how I could possibly make a living "chasing lizards." He gently suggested that perhaps a career in medicine would be a more practical way for me to follow my interest in biology. Nonetheless, my parents encouraged all their children to pursue their interests. My brother started building computers, and my sister became the physician that my father once hoped I would be. I just kept learning everything I could about the spectacular life on our planet, and I never grew out of that childhood fascination.

When it came time to go to college, I gravitated back to the Texas Hill Country, where my love of biodiversity was first ignited. Or, at least as close as I could get to it: I attended Baylor University in Waco, enrolling as a biology major. Even before starting classes in my freshman year, I traveled to Big Bend and then across the Hill Country, and floated down the Frio River at Garner State Park. My first semester, I went to work in the university's natural history museum, named after the early Texas naturalist and herpetologist

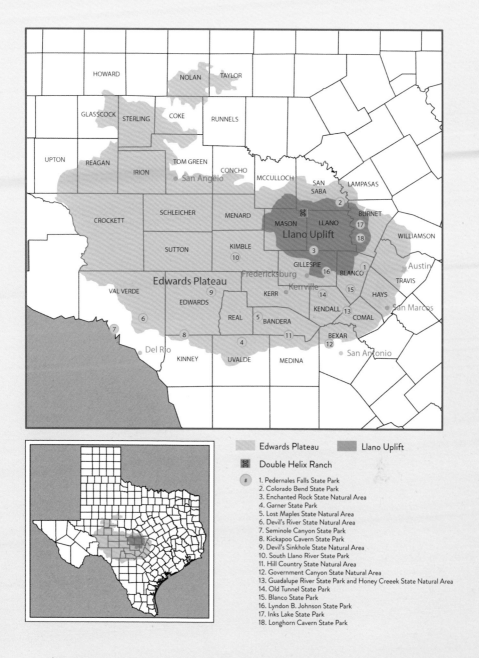

λ The Edwards Plateau Ecological Region, including the Llano Uplift and Edwards Plateau. Together, these regions are informally known as the Texas Hill Country. The locations of the Double Helix Ranch, major cities and towns, and state parks and natural areas are indicated.

John K. Strecker. This afforded me many opportunities for field trips with dedicated naturalists in the Biology Department, as well as with groups of like-minded fellow students. On my first free weekend, I traveled to Enchanted Rock on the Llano Uplift near Fredericksburg, which was at that time a privately owned campground (it would later become Enchanted Rock State Natural Area). The beauty and diversity of the area resonated with me, and I knew that somehow, for me, this was home. Through college, I spent virtually all my free time traveling through the Hill Country, learning about its plants and animals, floating down its rivers, camping in its parks, and thinking about life.

I met my wife, Ann, at Baylor, and for our first date, I asked her to accompany me to look for frogs in a violent rainstorm. Several days earlier, I'd invited her to come up to my dorm room to listen to my records of frog calls. She turned that initial invitation down, saying that her mother had warned her about people like me, but her roommate accepted my invitation. Ann said later that she was surprised to learn that I had actually played records of frog calls for her roommate. So when it started raining, I called Ann and asked her to meet me in front of her dorm. She jumped into my car to get out of the rain, while protesting that no one should venture out in such weather, and we were on our way. Although she never learned to love frogs as much as I do, she seemed to enjoy my enthusiasm for all things biological. Soon, she was joining me on my forays and camping trips across the Texas Hill Country, and especially to Enchanted Rock.

Ann and I married, and then after graduation from Baylor we moved to the University of Kansas for my graduate school training. After I earned my Ph.D. studying the genetics of frog diversity and evolution, we moved to the University of Miami, where I was first employed as an assistant professor of biology. Ann and I loved scuba-diving in the Florida Keys and Caribbean, and I enjoyed the wilds of the Everglades, but it never felt like home. After a few years, when a faculty job in zoology opened up at the University of Texas at Austin, I immediately applied. The next year, we moved to Austin, and I have been on the faculty there ever since. After terms directing the School of Biological Sciences and the Center for Computational Biology and Bioinformatics, I now serve as director of the University of Texas Biodiversity Center, which supports research, education, and public outreach about the Earth's biodiversity.

Austin is a wonderful place to live, but above all else, to me it is the front porch of the Edwards Plateau. Almost immediately after moving to Austin, Ann and I bought some acreage along a limestone creek near Pedernales Falls State Park in Blanco County, which we named Girraween (an Australian Aboriginal word that means "place of flowers"). Our two sons, Erec and Jonathan, grew up playing in the creek and woods of Girraween, and Jonathan lives there today with his wife, Lauren. Jonathan is building online creative communities for people who want to live in and work from beautiful, remote places. Erec now owns and directs a summer camp on the Hill Country's Highland Lakes, known as Camp Champions, which reconnects children of all ages to the natural world and gets them away from smart phones and computer screens for a few weeks.

As soon as Ann and I could afford a larger ranch, we were drawn farther out into the Hill Country, to our beloved Llano Uplift. We named our new property the Double Helix Ranch, in reference to my research on the genetic mechanisms that give rise to Earth's biodiversity. We now spend as much of our lives as possible at the Double Helix.

Over time, we have continued to add on to the Double Helix Ranch as neighboring properties come up for sale. Our goal has been to preserve and restore the biodiversity of the ranch and surrounding area as much as possible. We operate it as a functional cattle ranch, raising Texas Longhorn cattle, in part to demonstrate that a cattle ranch in the area can operate, and even thrive, while still protecting and restoring its native plants and animals. We've now developed cooperative biodiversity restoration projects with several of our largest ranch neighbors.

All the electricity on the Double Helix Ranch, including that used to charge our electric vehicles, comes from solar power, and we return excess solar power production to the grid every month of the year. Rainwater is captured from rooftops, and we use solar power to pump water from wells. Our cattle are range-fed, and they fill the role that native bison once served in helping us to maintain healthy grasslands. We avoid pesticides and herbicides on the ranch, instead using biological principles to maintain a balance in the local ecosystem. For example, our thriving populations of dung beetles clean and bury all the cattle dung from our pastures, thus fertilizing our pastures even as they clean them.

This book is a collection of essays about the spectacular life of the Texas Hill Country, including both familiar and loved species, as well as ones that few people have ever seen or heard about. It is also about my personal efforts over many decades to discover, preserve, and restore the natural beauty of the area. My nearly life-long engagement with the land, waters, animals, and plants of the Hill Country is the source of the stories of this book. I hope the book will be of interest to nature lovers of all kinds, to residents and visitors to the Hill Country, to people who hunt and fish for recreation and to be outdoors, and to ranch owners who are seeking to preserve, protect, and restore the beauty of the land that they love.

1

Geological Setting of the Edwards Plateau

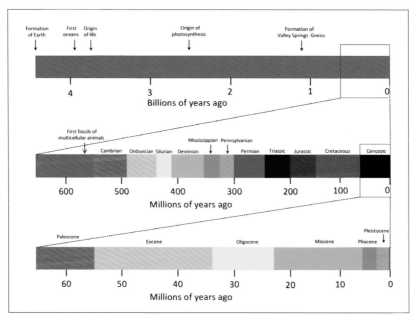

Geological time line of the Earth.

On a perfect, sunny spring day, shortly after we bought a new section of the Double Helix Ranch, I was exploring a ranch creek with my sons. Jonathan and Erec were 10 and 13 at the time—old enough to explore on their own, and still young enough to be enthusiastic about everything. The boys ran ahead as I looked for snakes and frogs along the creek. Suddenly, they came running back, excitedly describing a beautiful rock canyon they had found. They proudly led me forward to see their discovery.

Jonathan and Erec took me to a place where the creek had carved graceful contours into the surrounding rock, revealing twisted layers of gneiss and giant dikes filled with quartz and gemstones, including isolated crystals of black tourmaline, blue topaz, and purple sapphire. We all marveled at the beauty of the rocks that had been exposed by millions of years of water erosion. Jonathan and Erec were fascinated with the complex and striking geology; they wanted to know how these rocks and gemstones had formed.

The rocks that particularly caught our attention were exposures of Valley Springs Gneiss (pronounced "nice"), which first formed well over a billion years ago. These are among the oldest rocks of the Llano Uplift, located in the north-central part of the Edwards Plateau. When the sediments that formed Valley Springs Gneiss were deposited, this area was off the southern coast of an ancient equatorial continent known as Laurentia.

There was life in that ancient sea off coastal Laurentia, but it was mostly microscopic. Many of the small aquatic life forms were

Gemstones from the Double Helix Ranch. *Upper left*, blue topaz; *upper right*, smoky quartz; *lower left*, black tourmaline; *lower right*, iron pyrite; *center*, star sapphire.

photosynthetic, and they were slowly releasing oxygen into the Earth's atmosphere. Nonetheless, atmospheric oxygen levels were a tiny fraction of what they are today. There was not yet much, if any, terrestrial life on Laurentia, or anywhere else on Earth for that matter.

With no plants to hold back erosion, the granitic rocks of Laurentia eroded into the sea and accumulated on the ocean floor. Then, around 1.1 billion years ago, another landmass (which would eventually become South America) slowly but steadily collided with the southern coast of Laurentia, in a meeting of two tectonic plates. The intense heat and pressure from this tectonic collision transformed the granitic coastal sediments of Laurentia into gneiss and forced them upward into an ancient mountain range. Cracks in the gneiss filled with magma, which slowly cooled to form crystals of quartz and various gemstones. These crystal-filled cracks, known as pegmatites, were what my sons and I now could see as dikes running through the gneiss.

This collision of continents also resulted in the release of larger quantities of magma that formed the younger granites of the Llano Uplift, which are about a billion years old. Most prominent of these is Town Mountain Granite, the pink Texas granite that is widely used in construction, including for the Texas Capitol Building. It is also the rock that makes up Enchanted Rock, in the popular Enchanted Rock State Natural Area. The average crystal size in granite is larger than in gneiss, so it erodes into coarse granite gravel of feldspar, quartz, and mica, rather than into the fine sands that are typical around gneiss outcrops.

Today, remnants of this ancient mountain range—formed from the collision of continents—extend north and east from the Llano Uplift, through the Ouachitas, Ozarks, Appalachians, and all the way across the modern Atlantic Ocean to the hills of Scotland. After the collision that produced these mountains, other continental landmasses continued to collide with Laurentia. By 750 million years ago, most of the Earth's continents had formed one gigantic landmass, called Rodinia by today's geologists.

The formation of the super-continent Rodinia may have been

the first step that resulted in a massive cooling of the Earth's climate for many millions of years. Geologists call this great cooling the Cryogenian period; it is known more colloquially as Snowball Earth. During this time, most of the Earth was covered in ice, and glaciers covered most of the land surfaces.

The Earth's surface is always in one of two states: rock layers are either being formed (deposition), or they are being eroded away (erosion). Across all of Laurentia, massive glaciation during the Snowball Earth period (about 710–640 million years ago) was associated with large-scale erosion. Extending even further in time in both directions from the Snowball Earth period, from about 1 billion years ago until the beginning of the Cambrian period 541 million years ago, erosional processes dominated across many of the Earth's continents, including Laurentia.

The gap in deposition of rock strata between about 1 billion and 541 million years ago produced what is now called the Great Unconformity, evidence of which can be seen in many parts of the world today. In some regions, the rock strata are fairly continuous across this time span, but the Great Unconformity is widespread and is evident in many places in North America. On the Double Helix Ranch, this geological gap occurs between Precambrian Valley Springs Gneiss and Cambrian-aged Hickory Sandstone.

Hickory Sandstone started forming more than half a billion years ago, directly on top of the 1.1-billion-year-old Valley Springs Gneiss. By the middle of the Cambrian, the ancient mountain range formed by continental collisions had been eroded and covered once more with a shallow sea, so sediments once again began to accumulate. The Cambrian is very important from a paleobiological perspective, because of the rapid proliferation of multicellular animals that took place near the beginning of this period, informally called the Cambrian Explosion.

Some layers of the Hickory Sandstone have few identifiable fossils, probably because they were deposited when the seas were relatively deep. But there are also thin layers of highly fossiliferous siltstones, which represent shallow estuaries and coastal flats that were teeming with animal life. There are abundant casts and trace fossils of various soft-bodied invertebrates, as well as tracks and remains of trilobites and other early arthropods.

When my sons and I found the area on the Double Helix Ranch where the strikingly different rock layers meet at the Great Unconformity, I showed Jonathan and Erec that they could cross about half a billion years of geological formations in a single step. Soon they were leaping back and forth between the strata, happily counting up the billions of years they were traversing.

As we step from the Precambrian gneiss onto the Cambrian sandstone, one of the most obvious changes, in addition to the sudden presence of fossilized multicellular organisms, is the inclusion in the sandstone of deep red deposits of iron and manganese oxides. The oxides were formed in an oxygen-rich atmosphere produced by all the photosynthesis in the warming seas that followed Snowball Earth.

Å The Seaquist House in Mason, Texas, one of the early German settlements on the Edwards Plateau. The reddish brown building material is Hickory Sandstone.

Hickory Sandstone is widely used as a building material to the west of the Llano Uplift. If you visit one of the German-settled Hill Country towns near the Llano Uplift (such as Fredericksburg or Mason), you will see that many of the picturesque stone buildings are made from hand-quarried Hickory Sandstone, carved and set by German stonemasons in the mid- and late 1800s. This rock formation also contains the Hickory Aquifer, which supplies much of the northwestern portion of the Hill Country with groundwater.

The Cambrian Explosion of life recorded in Hickory Sandstone was brought about by the warming of the planet and the rapid accumulation of oxygen in the atmosphere produced by early photosynthetic organisms. The higher oxygen concentrations allowed large, multicellular organisms to exist, diversify, and thrive. The iron oxides that give Hickory Sandstone its characteristic reddish coloration formed as the higher oxygen concentrations led to oxidation of iron in ancient Cambrian seas.

Along portions of the Llano and James Rivers south of Mason, as well as along portions of the San Saba River to the north, there is another, younger Cambrian rock layer known as the Wilberns Formation. A major point of interest in this formation is the presence of large fossil stromatolites, which are the remains of enormous layered colonies of cyanobacteria (blue-green algae). Some of these fossil stromatolites are taller than an adult human.

The ancient rocks of the Llano Uplift are encircled by progressively younger rock layers. If you are interested in finding fossils, some of the best formations in the Hill Country are limestones that were deposited in the Ordovician (485–443 million years ago) and Devonian (419–359 million years ago) Periods. The Ordovician limestones of the Ellenburger Group contain another important aquifer, the Ellenberger–San Saba Aquifer, which nearly surrounds the Llano Uplift. These rock layers also contain fossils of trilobites, gastropods, cephalopods, and other marine life. Most of these fossils are preserved in nodules of chert. Just above the Ellenburger Group is a thin layer of Devonian rock known as the Bear Spring Formation, which can be found in isolated pockets near the Llano

Ʌ Crinoid fossils in the Bear Spring Formation, Devonian Period, Mason County, Texas.

River. This formation contains abundant fossil remains of crinoid stems, which look like round disks stacked on top of one another.

The next youngest layers are limestones and sandstones of the Pennsylvanian and Mississippian ages (together about 359–299 million years ago). Some of these outcrops contain countless fossils of crinoids, brachiopods, and other marine organisms, whereas others contain numerous terrestrial plant fossils, such as tree ferns, horsetails, and club mosses. Our buildings at the Double Helix Ranch are constructed from quarried sandstones that are packed with fossil plants from this period.

The limestone strata that make up the geological feature called the Edwards Plateau extend in all directions surrounding the Llano Uplift. But the entire region of the Edwards Plateau and Llano Uplift taken together is known as the Edwards Plateau Ecological Region, which sometimes leads to confusion in communication. When geologists say "Edwards Plateau," they usually are referring to the geological formation of Cretaceous limestones; however, when most people use the term, they are referring to the geographic area known as the Edwards Plateau Ecological Region (or ecoregion), which includes the older rock formations of the Llano Uplift. In this book, unless I'm specifically discussing the geological formation, I'll use "Edwards Plateau" or "Hill Country" interchangeably to refer to the entire ecoregion.

Most of the geological formation called the Edwards Plateau consists of extensive deposits of Cretaceous limestone (formed 145.5–65.5 million years ago). In the Texas Hill Country these are often broken into Trinity (lower Cretaceous) and Edwards (upper Cretaceous) limestones and associated shales. There are many different named members within each of these two broad categories, and many of these form easily detectable strata throughout the Edwards Plateau. These distinct strata are readily visible in the numerous highway road cuts across the Hill Country.

The Cretaceous limestones are well known for their fossils, especially of gastropods, bivalves, rudists, echinoderms, and ammonites, but also of some large marine reptiles. Some layers, such as the Hensell Sand Formation (a conglomerate of pebbles and cobbles of older rocks), contain some interesting plant fossils (cycads) that grew on the shores of the broad Cretaceous sea that covered much of central Texas.

Many limestone formations contain nodules of chert that were widely used by native peoples to make spearpoints and other tools, which I sometimes find as I walk around the Double Helix Ranch. The Edwards and Trinity limestones also contain vast aquifers that supply water to most of the springs, streams, and rivers of the Hill Country, as well as providing the groundwater supplies for most of the human population in the area. The limestones of the Edwards Plateau are famous for extensive and beautiful cave formations.

Relatively few rock deposits in the Hill Country are younger than the Cretaceous, as erosion has dominated in the area over most of the past 50 million years. Most of the younger rock layers that persist are smaller, alluvial deposits of relatively recent age. The most extensive of these is the Sparta Sand Formation, deposited in the Eocene Epoch (56–34 million years ago). There are also alluvial deposits that date from the Pleistocene to the Holocene, deposited within just the past few million years. Some of them contain fossils of the Pleistocene megafauna, such as mammoths, ground sloths, and giant tortoises.

A short drive or a canoe trip along one of the many picturesque Hill Country rivers can easily take you on a tour across more than a billion years of geological history. If you take such a tour, notice that the Hill Country has been repeatedly covered by shallow seas teeming with marine life (when rock layers were deposited), alternating with periods where it has been uplifted into hills or mountains (when erosional processes dominated). This complex geological history is a major factor in understanding the Hill Country's present biological diversity.

2

From Acid Sands to Alkaline Clays

⋀ Primary soils of the Double Helix Ranch. *Left to right:* A soil high in clay content (the smallest particle size), a loam with similar proportions of all three particle sizes, a loam with similar proportions of silt and sand but little clay, and a very sandy soil (the largest particle size).

In contrast to rock outcrops, soils are typically quite young, having formed within the last few million years. Eventually some of these sediments will form new sedimentary rock layers. Soils consist largely of eroded rocks and minerals, mixed with varying degrees of organic matter. They also hold various amounts of water and gases (such as tiny pockets of air) and often a rich community of biological organisms. Which organisms can live in or around various soils depends on many factors, including how much water and air the soils receive and retain, the acidity or alkalinity of the soil, and how easily the soil is broken apart.

Rocks erode into different sizes of particles, depending on their composition. The tiniest particles (less than 0.002 mm) are known as clay particles. These particles fit closely together. When they get wet, they tend to hold on to the water, forming a barrier that does not drain or let additional water pass through. This feature makes clays useful for forming ponds and other wetlands, but it is hard for many plants and other organisms to thrive in heavy clay soils. Many plants struggle in clays because these soils drain poorly and tend to be alkaline (high pH). Tiny clay particles often leach through more porous surface layers to form clay horizons below the surface. In the Hill Country, caliche clay is especially likely to form from degraded limestone, although a subsurface layer of clay is often found in other areas as well.

Slightly larger soil particles (between 0.002 and 0.05 mm) are called silt, and even larger particles (between 0.05 and 2.0 mm) are called sand. Anything larger than that is gravel. The larger the particle size, the easier it is for water and air to flow through the soil. Soils get many of their characteristics from the relative proportions of clay, silt, and sand that they contain. Loams are mixtures of the three soil types, usually with less clay than silt or sand, and many plants grow best in loamy soil.

The surface soils of the Llano Uplift, which are formed from degraded granite and gneiss, contain very high proportions of sand. These sandy soils drain well and contain plenty of oxygen, but they retain water rather poorly. When it rains or the soils are irrigated, many plants grow quite well in sandy soils. On the other hand, sandy soils dry out quickly in a drought and are often deficient in some nutrients and organic matter. That is why plants that thrive in sandy soils tend to grow quickly when conditions are favorable and then die back or become dormant when they are not.

Different plants are adapted to different types of soil, and you may notice some obvious changes in vegetation as you move from one area of the Hill Country to another. It is easiest to notice this in the trees. For example, Ashe Juniper (locally known as "cedar") grows well in the thin, alkaline, loamy, and clayey soils found in areas of Edwards and Trinity limestones. These soils are often deposited directly over limestone (as in much of the eastern Edwards Plateau) or over limestone and caliche clay (across most of the western parts of the Edwards Plateau). In fact, juniper grows so well in these areas that it is considered problematic in many regions of limestone outcrops.

Juniper was naturally controlled by frequent wildfires, and it can be a highly flammable tree, especially when dry. But with the suppression of fire, juniper woodland can grow very dense and choke out other vegetation. Nonetheless, despite many local myths, the Ashe Juniper woodlands of the Plateau are not a recent phenomenon. The earliest European travelers to the region reported extensive regions of cedar brakes, and these juniper woodlands are an important habitat for many of the Hill Country's species. For example, the bark from mature juniper trees is an important nesting material for the Golden-cheeked Warbler, whose summer breeding ground is restricted to the area immediately in and around the Edwards Plateau.

You may notice, though, that Ashe Juniper is not abundant or invasive in regions of the Llano Uplift that have sandy soils formed from gneiss or granite. These rocks tend to erode into larger particle sizes, which allows rapid degradation of organic matter and leads to slightly acidic soils. Ashe Juniper grows poorly in these soils, rarely reaching maturity to reproduce. But Honey Mesquite thrives in these soils, and that is the tree that is more likely to spread in grasslands and other open areas in regions of the Hill Country with sandy soils.

Mesquite seeds generally need to pass through the stomach of a large mammal before they can germinate, so mesquite often becomes invasive in areas that are heavily grazed by cattle or other livestock. The sandy soils of the Double Helix Ranch are also favorable for Post Oak, Blackjack Oak, Black Hickory, and many other native trees that you will rarely see growing naturally in regions of the Hill Country with tight alkaline soils. There are also oaks that prefer the alkaline soils, such as Texas Red Oak, Lacey Oak, and Shin Oak. On the other hand, our most abundant oak species, Plateau Live Oak, seems to grow well across most of the different soil types of the Texas Hill Country.

Besides the obvious differences in tree cover, if you look more closely, you will find that we have many specialized species that are confined to an island of sandy soils in the Llano Uplift. This geological region of igneous and igneous-metamorphic rocks is surrounded by the limestones of the Edwards Plateau. Many species of plants and animals that are found here are isolated from their closest relatives that live in sandy soils of east or south Texas. That means that we have many endemic species in this area—species found here but nowhere else in the world. In another chapter, I'll describe the endemic Llano Uplift Sandmint, which you can find blooming in May along sandy creeks that run through areas of Valley Springs Gneiss. An animal example that is all too familiar to gardeners in sandy areas of the Llano Uplift is the endemic Llano Pocket Gopher, *Geomys texensis*. In yet another chapter, I'll describe some of the endemic species that live in the underground aquifers of the Hill Country.

In addition to soil differences, geology affects biological distributions in many other ways as well. The most obvious is that many plants and animals are restricted to various types of rock outcrops. Across the Hill Country, the dramatic outcrops of granite, gneiss, sandstone, and limestone are home to many species of reptiles, mammals, birds, and plants that are rarely, if ever, found very far away from rocky areas. Exploring the rocky outcrops of the Texas Hill Country may lead you to see species like Crevice Spiny Lizards, Ringtails, Canyon Wrens, and the beautiful purple flowers of Eggleaf Skullcap.

When I explore the Texas Hill Country, I enjoy noting the changes in species of plants and animals as I move from one geological formation to another. It is easy to see how geology influences the local soils and aquifers, and how these features influence the local dominant vegetation, which in turn influences which animals are likely to be found in the area. All these changes in geology, hydrology, and soils contribute to the high biological and geographic diversity of the Hill Country. It is this diversity that makes the region so attractive to naturalists, hikers, sportsmen and women, geologists, biologists, ranchers, and residents.

3

Hill Country Weather

Droughts, Floods, and Severe Storms

⅄ A Hill Country stream after a snowstorm.

The Texas Hill Country is well known for both severe droughts and devastating floods. We seem to go back and forth between these two states on a roughly five-year cycle. The average annual rainfall on the Edwards Plateau exhibits a steep gradient from about 35" (990 mm) in the east down to about 15" (380 mm) in the west.

Rainfall at the Double Helix Ranch averages in the upper middle of that range, at about 27" (685 mm). But an "average" year is rare. Instead, most years are either well above the long-term average or well below it. It seems that we have either feast or famine when it comes to rainfall. Moreover, the droughts and wet periods often last across several years. We do have some seasonal patterns to our rainfall as well, but in the dry years, even the normally wet months see little rain. What causes these long-term cycles of drought and flood?

The biggest factor that affects rainfall in the Hill Country is the cycle of El Niño and La Niña (formally known as the El Niño Southern Oscillation, abbreviated ENSO). This refers to a regular oscillation in surface water temperature across the equatorial Pacific Ocean. Around once or twice a decade, the Pacific water surface along the equator cools by about 2–4°F (compared with the long-term average) as cold water from deep in the ocean moves to the surface. This cooling signals the arrival of a La Niña episode. The temperature change causes the Pacific Jet Stream to shift to the north, and major Pacific storm systems move across North America well to the north of Texas.

The biggest effect on our weather from the ENSO cycle occurs from October to March. We normally receive about half of our average annual rainfall during those months, but in La Niña winters, our rainfall drops by more than half. In extreme cases, we may get as little as 2" or 3" (50–75 mm) of rain during that half of the year.

The flip side of La Niña is known as El Niño. In El Niño episodes, the surface of the equatorial Pacific warms 2–4°F over the long-term average, and the Pacific Jet Stream shifts to the south, bringing Pacific storms and moisture directly over Texas. Under those conditions, we tend to have very wet winters, with twice or more our average rainfall.

Although the ENSO cycle most directly affects our rainfall from October to March, our summer rainfall can also be influenced by this cycle. First, summer rainfall depends to some extent on local conditions, and a wet winter can lead to a wet summer. The reason is that there is more moisture available to evaporate into the atmosphere, so wet conditions tend to lead to more rainfall. Literally, when it rains, it pours.

The second effect on our summer rainfall depends on how the ENSO cycle influences the Atlantic tropical storm season. El Niño years tend to suppress tropical storms in the Atlantic, whereas the storm season tends to be more active in La Niña conditions. In some years ENSO may have little effect on central Texas, or it can lead to extreme floods when a hurricane stalls out over the Edwards Plateau. When the latter happens in the summer following a long, dry La Niña winter, the Hill Country can be thrown suddenly from a drought into flood conditions.

Hill Country rivers and streams are prone to flash floods, which account for a large fraction of accidental deaths in the area. Extreme events, such as stalled hurricanes moving in off the Gulf of Mexico or supercell thunderstorms that move north into the Hill Country after forming over the mountains of Coahuila, Mexico, have been recorded that dumped an average year's rainfall in a single day. Even much smaller amounts can and do cause flash floods. Low-water crossings are common across the region, and rivers can rise several feet in seconds during an extreme rain event. Hill Country towns along the Llano, Guadalupe, Blanco, and other major rivers often memorialize historic flood events with high-water marks on local buildings.

Long-term residents of the Hill Country also likely remember the devastating drought of the early 1950s, which was brought on by back-to-back La Niñas in 1950–1951 and 1954–1956. The five-year period from 1951 to 1956 was the longest and most severe Hill Country drought recorded since weather data have been kept. There have been other severe droughts during each of the decades since then, when additional La Niña episodes led to periods of greatly decreased rainfall. Of these, the most memorable was the drought that began in the fall of 2010 and continued through 2011. In the 12 months from October 1, 2010, through September 30, 2011, only 5.36" (134 mm) of rain fell on the Double Helix Ranch (and similar small amounts fell throughout the region). That was the lowest 12-month total in recorded history. Many centuries-old oak trees died in that record drought, and their dead trunks will stand out on the landscape for decades to come. The 2010–2011 drought did not last nearly as long as the drought of the early 1950s, but it was a drier one-year period than any year during the 1950s.

In contrast, the most rain ever recorded in a 12-month period at the Double Helix Ranch was 51.0" (1,295 mm), during the El Niño episode of 1997–1998. That was the strongest El Niño of the past century. Most Hill Country ranchers probably feel that we have many more droughts than wet periods, but in reality, El Niños occur about as often as La Niñas—on average once every five years. It is remarkable that these cycles can lead to almost a tenfold difference in our annual rainfall (5.36"–51.0", or 134 mm–1,295 mm). That range is as great as the difference in the average annual rainfall between the swamps of the Big Thicket in east Texas and the driest part of the Chihuahuan Desert in far west Texas.

Most Hill Country precipitation falls in the form of rain, but snowfall, freezing rain, and hailstorms occur nearly every year somewhere in the region. In spring 2021, the Double Helix Ranch was right in the bull's-eye of a devastating hailstorm, and we were pummeled for 20 minutes with 2- to 3-inch hailstones that caused considerable damage. All our trees had been leafing out and were green before the storm, but they were stripped bare by the hailstones. Developing fruit, new leaves, and even bark was ripped from the trees. Hailstones crashed through ranch-house windows, dented roofs and cars, gouged wood on outbuildings, punched through the walls of our chicken coop, and sent animals running for any cover they could find. Because heavy winds were blowing hailstones almost horizontally, many prickly pear cactus pads looked as if they had been used for target practice. By the end of the storm, the landscape looked as if it had been carpet-bombed.

Damage from a hailstorm depends largely on the size of the hailstones that fall. Larger hailstones are not just heavier but also fall to the ground at a much higher terminal velocity than do small stones. The reason for their faster rate of fall is the lower air resistance of larger hailstones relative to their mass. Air resistance increases as a function of the square of the radius of the object (the cross-section of the stone, or roughly the area of a circle), whereas a hailstone's weight or volume increases much faster, as a function of the cube of its radius. In a vacuum, a small stone and a large stone (or even a snowflake) would fall at the same rate because of the lack of air resistance, but we don't live in a vacuum.

In free fall in Earth's atmosphere, a pea-sized hailstone falls at about 18 miles per hour. In contrast, a hailstone 8 times the diameter (about 3") falls at around 110 miles per hour (if not driven even faster by wind). The 3" hailstone is also more than 500 times the weight of the smaller hailstone, even though it is only 8 times greater in diameter. Therefore, the 3" hailstone is moving 6 times as fast and weighs more than 500 times as much as the pea-sized hailstone. That means that the larger hailstone will strike a surface with about 3,000 times the force of the small one. That's why a walk through a hailstorm with pea-sized hail will be merely unpleasant, whereas large hailstones can easily be lethal.

Hailstones form in cumulonimbus clouds, commonly known as thunderheads or thunderstorm clouds. These clouds contain strong updrafts that can carry water droplets and ice particles up for many thousands of feet above the surface of the Earth. If you break a hailstone open, you are likely to see alternating layers of translucent and opaque ice. It was once thought that these layers were evidence that hailstones form by repeatedly rising and falling through a thundercloud. That turns out to be unnecessary. Hailstones can rise thousands of feet on updrafts and may be blown upward for 30 minutes or more. Then, as they fall through more freezing conditions, they continue to accumulate ice. When they pass through regions of the clouds with many supercooled water droplets, the water droplets freeze on the hailstone, forming translucent ice (with few pockets of air). When the hailstone rises or falls through parts of the cloud that contain only water vapor, small pockets of air are captured within the ice, which make it opaque. Thus, the layering represents different conditions experienced by the hailstone as it grows within different regions of the thundercloud, even if it only rises and falls a single time.

The air in a thunderstorm cloud is saturated with supercooled water vapor. Water needs a nongaseous (solid or liquid) surface on which to condense. Initially, water droplets condense on tiny bits of dust, salt crystals, or organic aerosols, or sometimes even on airborne bacteria. The water droplets then freeze into hailstones, which grow as they come into contact with more water droplets or water vapor.

Thunderstorms usually form in the spring and summer, when ground temperatures are well above freezing. But dry air moving into a thunderstorm promotes the conditions needed for hail, as the evaporative cooling that results can create freezing conditions relatively close to the ground. That's why hail is much more common at midlatitudes, such as in Texas, than it is in most areas of the Tropics, even though thunderstorms are more common in the Tropics. In the Tropics, the air within a thunderstorm usually is not cold enough for ice formation, except at very high altitudes. Hail in the Tropics is common only in mountainous regions, where the ground is closer to the freezing temperatures in the thunderhead.

The plants and animals of the Hill Country need to survive more than just droughts, floods, snow, and hail. Temperatures can range from below 0°F (−18°C) in the winter to above 110°F (43°C) in the summer. Although the extremes on both ends are rare, species that cannot survive or avoid such highs and lows are unlikely to persist over time on the Edwards Plateau. The wide range of possible temperatures and rainfall conditions select for hardy species that can survive a wide range of physiological conditions.

4

Some Texas Icons Haven't Been Here All That Long

⋏ A Collared Peccary, locally known as a javelina. Now part of the Texas landscape, this species moved north into Texas only in the 1700s. *Photo courtesy of Lawrence Gilbert.*

When you think about iconic Texas animals, the Nine-banded Armadillo and the Collared Peccary (also known as a javelina) are probably high on your mental list. But did you know that both of these animals are actually relatively recent immigrants to Texas?

In 1880, a biologist by the name of Edward Drinker Cope wrote a paper, published by the Smithsonian Institution in Washington, DC, titled "On the Zoological Position of Texas." The point of the paper was to determine the boundaries of the major biological realms of North America—where east meets west and north meets south. Cope reasoned that these boundaries must lie in Texas, and he visited the state in the late 1870s to see for himself. He traveled throughout Texas, and on one trip left San Antonio, taking what was then the main road west, which took him across the Edwards Plateau to near the headwaters of the Llano River, south of present-day Junction.

Why should we be interested in Cope's paper, written nearly a century and a half ago? It provides a fascinating window into the many changes that have occurred to the fauna of Texas, in the course of just a few human generations. For example, Cope reported that Jaguars were "not rare" along the Nueces, Medina, and Guadalupe rivers, and he saw many skins of locally killed Jaguars for sale in San Antonio. He reported Ocelots to be even more abundant and widely distributed than Jaguars, and he found them to be "common" near Fredericksburg. He noted that Mountain Lions were common "all over Texas."

Although Cope saw many mammals (like the wild cats mentioned above) that we now consider rare or extinct in Texas, he never saw an armadillo here, although he heard a report of one in Frio City (now Frio Town), in South Texas. In fact, armadillos had only recently moved north into Texas from Mexico when Cope made his surveys of Texas in the latter part of the nineteenth century. Cope did see Collared Peccaries, another iconic Texas mammal that moved north into our state only in the 1700s.

Both armadillos and javelinas are among the many animals that moved between North and South America as part of the Great American Interchange, a shift that occurred when the Panamanian Isthmus formed between the two continents nearly 3 million years ago. Once a land bridge connected North and South America, many animals moved in both directions between the two continents. In addition to armadillos, opossums and porcupines also moved north into North America from South America. Even more mammals—including Jaguars and other cats, as well as peccaries—moved from North America into South America than moved in the opposite direction.

Although armadillos entered Central America millions of years ago, it wasn't until the 1800s that the Nine-banded Armadillo made it as far north as Texas. Human agriculture and other human modifications of habitat almost certainly aided the expansion of armadillos northward and eastward, and they have continued to expand their range.

In their original tropical range in the Americas, armadillos rely heavily on a diet of ants. As they moved northward, however, they expanded their diet to include a broader array of small invertebrates and even some plants. That was an important adaptation, because a diet of ants would not allow armadillos to survive our northern winters. Diversifying their diets allowed armadillos to find food sources year-round and to put on enough fat to survive periods of inactivity during the coldest periods of the year. A study published in 2019 showed that the armadillo skull structure in recently invaded regions of North America has also evolved in a number of ways that are likely associated with the increased diversity in the animals' diets.

Armadillos are fascinating for many other reasons as well. One of the most interesting aspects of their biology is that armadillo offspring are typically identical quadruplets. The four siblings are only about three ounces each when born. After the young are born, usually in March, they stay in the burrow for the first three months of life, living only on their mother's milk. Sometime in June, they finally emerge and forage with the mother, staying with her for the rest of the summer and fall. By the time they reach one year old, they are independent and foraging on their own.

Armadillos are protected by a shell that consists of bony plates covered with scutes, which leads many people to mistake them for reptiles rather than mammals. But if you turn an armadillo over, you will see that its undersides are covered in rough hair, and as we have already noted, they produce milk like other mammals and give birth to live young.

The shell of an armadillo makes the animal heavier than water, so armadillos don't swim. Instead, they cross streams and rivers by holding their breath and walking across the bottom of the riverbed.

It is startling to follow an armadillo and watch it enter a water body and walk across the bottom.

Armadillos don't see well at distances, which allows potential predators to approach them closely before the armadillo reacts. When they sense danger, they may leap straight up in the air to escape. This is an unfortunate adaptation if the perceived danger is a passing car or truck; many an armadillo leaps to its death as it is hit by a passing vehicle. Once an armadillo is alarmed, it can move at surprising speeds to escape.

When I see an armadillo out and about on the Double Helix, I often try to approach it slowly and quietly from the rear, which allows me to follow it unnoticed as it forages. On several occasions, I've watched armadillos gathering leaves and other materials for their nests, which is quite a funny sight to behold. While holding the nesting material between its fore and hind limbs, the armadillo will hop backward to the nest in a highly comical manner. If you don't make any sudden movements, the armadillo is likely to smell you before it sees you. If you continue watching in this manner, you can follow an armadillo closely for many minutes before it senses your presence, and you will likely gain an increased understanding and enjoyment of this Texas icon.

5

Hill Country Endemics

⋀ Llano Uplift Sandmint (*Brazoria enquistii*), a wildflower species found only in the Llano Uplift region of the Edwards Plateau. It was first described in 2003.

Many people assume that most of Earth's plants and animals have been discovered and named by biologists. There are about 1.8 million living species that have been discovered on our planet to date. But did you know that biologists think there are far more undiscovered species than there are known species?

Some groups of plants and animals are thoroughly studied, whereas others are not, and some places on Earth are much better studied than others, from a biological point of view. Only a few groups of organisms are so well known that we think we have discovered virtually all of their living species. Mammals, birds, and butterflies are examples of groups that have been intensely studied all over the planet, to the point that we think almost all the species have been discovered and described. Still, even in these well-known groups, occasional surprises turn up.

Almost certainly there are many undiscovered species in the Texas Hill Country, but most of them are thought to be relatively small and hard to study. Fungi, tiny worms called nematodes, less conspicuous groups of insects, and bacteria are examples of poorly known groups that probably have many undiscovered species on the Edwards Plateau. Strange animals that live underground in the Trinity and Edwards aquifers are still being discovered and described, including a highly unusual radiation of groundwater salamanders (*Eurycea*), as well as numerous groups of invertebrates.

I often invite specialists to the Double Helix Ranch to collect and study their biological group of interest, and several visitors have discovered new species, previously unknown to science. For example, Dr. Jack Neff, one of the world's leading bee experts, found a previously unknown species of cuckoo bee on our ranch. He named the bee *Holcopasites jerryrozeni*, in honor of another famous bee biologist from the American Museum of Natural History. The first part of the scientific name, the genus, tells us that this kind of bee belongs to the larger group known as cuckoo bees. The second part of the name refers to the particular species within the cuckoo bee genus—in this case, Rozen's Cuckoo Bee.

Sometimes, however, even striking and obvious species can escape the notice of biologists, usually because the organisms live in specialized habitats or inaccessible areas. That was the case (until recently) with the beautiful Llano Uplift Sandmint, which lives only in a few Hill Country counties. This gorgeous flower is very particular about where it grows. It is found only along stream banks, in loose sands that are formed from degraded Valley Springs Gneiss (the dominant rock in the northern part of the Llano Uplift). This flower can be seen blooming in May along the sandy banks of major creeks in this area. It grows nowhere else in the world. I'm sure that some longtime Hill Country residents were familiar with this beautiful flower, but it was not formally described and named by scientists until 2003. Some of the first specimens that formed the basis of that description came from our Double Helix Ranch.

To describe a species as new to science, biologists must compare specimens of the new species to specimens of other related species. These reference specimens are housed in the world's biodiversity museums, such as the ones in the Biodiversity Center at the University of Texas at Austin. The biologist then writes a species description, which is a scientific article that describes what the new species looks like (usually with detailed illustrations) and how it is different from other known species. The article also proposes a unique scientific name and provides as much information as the biologist has learned about the new species. In the case of the Llano Uplift Sandmint, the new name chosen was *Brazoria enquistii,* in honor of Marshall Enquist, the author of a popular field guide to Texas Hill Country wildflowers.

New species may also be named for a distinguishing attribute, or in reference to where the new species was first discovered or other aspects related to the new species. For example, my collaborators and I named the Austin Blind Salamander *Eurycea waterlooensis,* meaning "of Waterloo," in reference to the original name for the settlement next to Barton Springs, which would later become Austin. We named another new salamander of the Hill Country *E. tonkawae,* in reference to the Tonkawa people, who originally shared the rock shelters and springs with this endemic amphibian. When we described a rare new salamander from remnants of habitat on the eastern margin of the Edwards Plateau, surrounded by sprawling human development along the Interstate 35 corridor, we chose the name *E. naufragia*, which means "remnants."

Once a species is named, then biologists begin to collect more information about it, and the name is useful for associating that information with each unique species. Some new species produce novel compounds that may be useful as pharmaceuticals or have other practical uses. Others may play important roles in local ecosystems. Understanding how local communities function becomes more feasible as biologists identify all the living participants. Of course, people may also appreciate the natural beauty of a rare species that can be seen only in a limited area. You may find it exciting to see and identify a Llano Uplift Sandmint in flower, if you realize that you are one of the few people on Earth lucky enough to see and admire this beautiful flower.

6

What Is the Value of Biodiversity?

⋏ An early summer display of wildflowers on the Double Helix Ranch.

learn a great deal from discussions with my ranch neighbors, especially my friend Hal Zesch. The Zesches were among the first German families to settle in the central Hill Country in the mid-1800s. Today they are known throughout the area for their stewardship of their family ranches, which have been protected, managed, enjoyed, and passed down through several generations. Butch Zesch, Hal's grandfather, understood the importance of native biodiversity and passed that understanding on to his son Jordan and to his grandson Hal, just as Hal and his wife, Amy, are conveying it to their children and grandchildren. Thanks to generations of families like the Zesches, much of the natural beauty of their region of the Hill Country has been preserved and protected. For many people, the inherent value of biodiversity seems obvious. Why, then, have we lost so much of our biodiversity? Clearly, everyone does not view biodiversity in the same light.

The question "What is the value of biodiversity?" may be answered in many ways. Here I'll approach it from biological, economic, and aesthetic viewpoints, and of course all of these viewpoints overlap and interact.

From a biological viewpoint, an ecosystem is like a complex machine, with many working parts. All the bacteria, fungi, plants, animals, and other living organisms interact with one another and with their physical environment to produce a functioning ecosystem. Bacteria and fungi provide critical resources that allow plants to grow and thrive. Plants convert carbon dioxide and water into sugars through photosynthesis. Animals recycle those nutrients back into the ecosystem through herbivory and predation. A healthy, functioning system requires a delicate balance of many different species from all these groups interacting with one another, in the context of the geology and hydrology of the land.

All those species of organisms—the various living parts of the complex ecosystem—are what make up biodiversity. Just like the parts of a complex machine, the different species are needed for the ecosystem to function well. Each species plays a role in the ecosystem. If we start to lose species, it is like losing parts off an automobile engine. The car may still run for a while, but it probably won't run as well, and eventually, if we lose enough parts, the car will stop working altogether. The same is true of ecosystems. Ecosystem productivity and stability are directly related to biodiversity. When we lose biodiversity, the ecosystem begins to collapse. The ecosystem is what makes life possible, and biodiversity is what makes the ecosystem function.

We can also make an argument on strictly economic grounds for the importance of biodiversity. The economy of the Texas Hill Country is based in large part (directly or indirectly) on income from ranching, hunting, and tourism. The indirect part comes from businesses and services (restaurants, auto services, retail, real estate, entertainment, etc.) that cater to ranchers, hunters, and tourists. Each of these enterprises depends on the biodiversity of the Hill Country. Ranchers benefit from healthy rangelands, which produce the livestock they raise. Healthy rangelands come from efficient and stable ecosystems, which are a product of biodiversity. Grass for cattle does not grow in isolation from other species. The long-term maintenance of grasslands requires a complex web of many species of bacteria, fungi, plants, and animals. Snakes are important to keep populations of rodents in check, just as bats, lizards, and frogs are important to control insect populations. An efficient, profitable ranch depends directly on overall biodiversity.

The land stewardship of the Zesch Ranch has resulted in a solid economic payback. The family has managed grazing to allow the restoration of native tallgrasses and broad-leaved forbs. Better habitat and management led to larger deer, which meant that hunting income rapidly increased. The hunters now bring their spouses and children to see the beautiful birds and other animals that have returned, and they pay more to do this. The changes also improved conditions for cattle; steers consistently gain about 400 pounds per animal between January and June. What makes it all possible is the balance and variety of native plants and animals (that is, biodiversity). The thick, deep roots of tallgrasses and perennial forbs soften the ground to such a degree that more than twice as much rain is absorbed deep into the ground as runs off. The filtered sunlight from the grass and forb cover substantially reduces evaporation of previous rainfall. Excess woody brush is contained by periodic prescribed burns, just as occurred here naturally for thousands of years before wildfires were suppressed.

Hunters come to the Hill Country not just to harvest deer and other game animals but also for the experience of a diverse and vibrant landscape. If obtaining venison was the only purpose of hunting, people could purchase nonnative, pen-raised deer from game farms. That is obviously not the main attraction of hunting. Hunting leases have replaced grazing leases as a primary source of income for many Hill Country landowners. The leases with the highest value are those that give hunters a chance to see a diverse and beautiful natural habitat, with plenty of wildlife. Of course, hunters want to see game animals, but most hunters want much more than that. Biodiversity is what gives extra value to a hunting lease.

Another major part of the Hill Country economy is tourism, and a big part of the draw is the area's natural beauty. Wildflower season brings people from far and wide to the Hill Country. Diverse native plant communities support birds, butterflies, and other wildlife of the Hill Country that are additional major draws. Visitors come to see the area's natural beauty, and then they spend money in area towns on food, hotels, shopping, and services. All of this economic activity depends on the natural beauty of the Hill Country, which stems in large part from our local biodiversity.

Finally, there is the aesthetic argument for the importance of biodiversity, which is the argument that resonates the most with me. Humans love variety. The beauty of a field of wildflowers comes in large part from the many colors, shapes, sizes, and textures that are present. We marvel at the antics of an armadillo, or the array of spines on a horny toad, or the beautiful call of Sandhill Cranes as they fly overhead. The sights, sounds, and smells of nature excite and stimulate us and also give us a sense of peace and happiness. We know from ancient rock art that humans have always been fascinated by and drawn to variety in nature.

People deprived of experiences in the natural world are said to suffer from an ailment called "nature deficit disorder." Most people need the natural beauty of biodiversity to feel whole and alive. That is why walking in the woods, strolling through a field of wildflowers, watching birds feed in your back yard, or canoeing down the Llano River feel so refreshing and rejuvenating. For most of us, the more varied our natural surroundings are, the happier we feel. We crave seeing natural variety in our lives, just as we crave variety in our diet and the types of entertainment we consume. Biodiversity is what makes the world such a beautiful place to live.

In short, biodiversity is what makes the Hill Country interesting, attractive, and economically viable for all its residents and visitors.

It is what gives us a sense of place, what makes the Edwards Plateau different and distinctive. Longtime residents like the Zesches know this intuitively, and pass a passion for the land and its inhabitants down through the generations. That love and appreciation for the beauty of our natural surroundings is something that benefits us all.

Sunrise at the Double Helix Ranch. ➤

II

THE SEASONAL LIFE OF A VERNAL POOL

The Edwards Plateau doesn't have any natural lakes, but many low spots fill seasonally with rainwater, especially in the spring. These temporary water bodies are known as vernal pools. Although they are not permanently wet, vernal pools with their seasonal waters are critical for the life cycles of a multitude of plants and animals. They can form on rock surfaces (as at the top of Enchanted Rock, in Llano County), in sandy fields, and in caliche pits. In grasslands, American Bison once created many vernal pools by wallowing in muddy spots, thereby digging out shallow depressions that would hold water in wet weather.

≺ A vernal pool on the Double Helix Ranch, shortly after filling.

Now that bison are largely gone from the landscape, the wallows are gradually filling in. Nonetheless, ranchers have more than made up for the absence of wallows by constructing seasonal stock tanks that catch rainwater. (Water bodies known as farm ponds elsewhere are called "tanks" in Texas.) The more permanent tanks are often stocked with fish, which prey on the numerous invertebrates that would otherwise live there. Some stock tanks dry up too often for fish to survive, however, and these shallow, seasonal tanks perform much the same ecological role that the bison wallows once did.

On the Double Helix Ranch, I've constructed numerous vernal pools by digging out wet spots, much as the bison would have formed them with their wallowing action. I deliberately keep them shallow so that they dry in the summer, which keeps aquatic predators from accumulating. When they fill, these pools attract a wide variety of fascinating plants and animals, some of which are described in the following chapters.

7

Tilting at Tiny Windmills

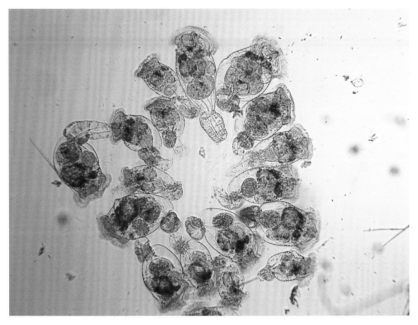

⋏ A cluster of rotifers as seen under a microscope. A corona (a crown of cilia) surrounds the head of each rotifer and looks like a spinning wheel on the live organisms. *Photo courtesy of Edward Theriot.*

When I was in primary school, my mother returned to college to finish her degree. I had a great time one year helping her collect samples for her zoology class. One week, her class assignment was to look for microscopic aquatic animals. I knew lots of promising water holes where all kinds of life likely thrived, so my mom went to class that week loaded down with many vials of water samples to examine and explore.

When my mother looked at the first sample through a home microscope, she almost immediately cried out, "It looks like there are hundreds of little windmills!" She let me take a look, and I saw long stalks capped with whirling circles that did indeed look a lot like miniature windmills. Later in class, my mother's zoology professor helped her identify the little windmill animals as rotifers.

The head of a rotifer is surrounded by a distinctive organ called the corona, which is Latin for "crown." The corona appears like a crown of cilia (hairlike projections) around the head of a rotifer, with the rotifer's mouth in the middle. The rotifer uses the cilia of the corona to sweep tiny food particles into its mouth and thus filter the water for sustenance.

Decades after that first encounter with rotifers, I learned that some species in this group have a fascinating life history that is something of mystery. Rotifers often live in temporarily wet places, and the adults live for only a few weeks. Although some species of rotifers have both males and females, only females are known in one group of rotifers. As far as anyone has been able to determine, the females in this group always produce offspring asexually by simply producing clones of themselves. Studies of rotifer genetics and rotifers fossilized in amber suggest that females in this group have been reproducing without any males around for at least tens of millions of years.

Why is this surprising? After all, asexual reproduction has some clear advantages from a population growth standpoint. Since all individuals in an asexual species are female, they can all produce offspring, so the reproductive rate of an asexual species is about twice as high as in a species where half the individuals are male.

If there is a twofold advantage in the reproductive rate of asexual reproduction, then why do most plants and animals reproduce sexually? The advantages of sexual reproduction have to do with genetic recombination—specifically, mixing and recombining the genes from two different parents. Genetic recombination produces greater genetic variation in a population, and it also produces a pathway to purge harmful mutations from the population.

When organisms replicate asexually, genetic mistakes (mutations) are introduced each time their genetic material is copied. That happens with sexual reproduction as well, but recombining multiple copies of genes from different parents produces offspring with and without the mutations. That makes it easier for natural selection to favor beneficial mutations and also to purge the harmful ones from the population.

When there is no genetic recombination (the expectation with asexual reproduction), each generation of offspring contains more genetic errors, and there is no way to keep harmful mutations from accumulating. Biologists call this phenomenon Muller's Ratchet— named after Hermann J. Muller, a famous University of Texas geneticist who first described the importance of genetic recombination in removing harmful mutations from a population. Muller also won a Nobel Prize for discovering the role that radiation plays in causing genetic mutations.

Mutations that allow asexual reproduction can have a short-term advantage, because they immediately increase the reproductive rate of the population, so asexual reproduction has arisen fairly often in evolutionary history. Even though asexual lineages may do well in the short term, they eventually falter as they accumulate too many harmful mutations over many generations.

The only way for an asexual lineage to survive over millions of years is if there is some other means of recombining the genome with genomes from other individuals of the species. For many years, that was the mystery of asexual rotifers: if they reproduce asexually, how do they manage to recombine their genomes and purge their populations of harmful mutations?

The answer turns out to be quite surprising. When wet rotifer habitat dries up, the tiny rotifers desiccate (dry out) and then rehydrate when water returns. As they dry, their genome is often broken into fragments, and the rotifers have special repair systems that put their genome back together again as they re-hydrate. In doing so, the rotifers can also take up small fragments of DNA from their environment. These bits of DNA include the remains of other rotifer genomes (from rotifers that did not survive the desiccation process). The rotifers then rebuild their genomes, incorporating some of the DNA from their deceased relatives in the process. In this way, they undergo genetic recombination among individuals, achieved without any sexual reproduction. (I do not recommend trying this at home if you are not a rotifer.)

As I learned from my mother's zoology class, there is a wide world of diverse plants and animals that can't be seen except under a microscope. The diversity we see with our naked eyes is only a small part of the living world. Those water samples I collected for my mother introduced me to an alien world full of bizarre, tiny animals—not just rotifers, but others with strange names like water bears and copepods. Peer into a drop of water from your local pond or river and you may discover a beautiful world where fascinating creatures float and swim around.

8

Crustacean Wonders

Ʌ Tadpole shrimp (*Triops*) from a vernal pool on the Double Helix Ranch.

Most summers, the seasonal wetlands around the Double Helix Ranch and across the Hill Country dry as the days get long and hot. When rains return and days cool, vernal pools quickly transform from seemingly lifeless mudflats to shallow pools packed with beautiful flowering plants and fascinating swimming animals. Many of these organisms survive in the dried mud as seeds or eggs. Others develop from eggs that are laid by flying insects that quickly find the newly filled ponds.

As vernal pools are wet only seasonally, they typically lack predatory fishes. This is critical for the survival of the multitudes of amphibians and invertebrates that rely on vernal pools to complete their life cycles. There are other predators in these pools, however. Wading birds, snakes, and raccoons regularly visit vernal pools to feast on developing tadpoles and aquatic invertebrates, as do giant predatory water bugs. The aquatic larvae of dragonflies are also fearsome predators in vernal pools.

In spring, after the vernal pools have filled, careful observers are likely to see several remarkable species of crustaceans (the group of shelled animals that includes familiar crabs, shrimp, crayfish, and lobsters). The most obvious of the vernal pool crustaceans you are likely to see are Fairy Shrimp, which are often present by the thousands. People often mistake schools of Fairy Shrimp for tiny fish, but if you look closely, you will see that each little animal has 11 pairs of swimming legs extending upward from the body. Fairy Shrimp grow up to an inch long and feed by filtering algae and small organic particles from the water. They rarely survive in the presence of fish, so they need seasonal pools to complete their development.

Vernal pools are often populated with tadpoles, the larvae of frogs and toads. Look closely, though, and you may notice that some are not tadpoles at all but instead are Tadpole Shrimp, a species of the genus *Triops* (meaning "three eyes"). *Triops* are so named because they have three eyes, including two large compound eyes that they use for forming images as well as a central simple eye on the top of their head that is used for detecting light and movement.

Triops species are found on all the world's continents except Antarctica, as well as on some isolated oceanic islands. How does a little crustacean that can live only in freshwater manage to colonize temporary pools over much of the Earth?

The adult stage of *Triops* lasts only a few months, during which the shrimp lay their eggs in the mud of their pools. When the pools dry, the tiny eggs become dormant. Highly resistant to heat and drying, the dormant eggs can tolerate temperatures close to that of boiling water. Most eggs remain in the dried mud until the pools refill, but they are small enough that they are easily blown in the wind as dust. The eggs can also be carried in mud on the feet of wading birds. Thus the eggs serve as a means of dispersal, and new vernal pools are quickly colonized.

Tadpole Shrimp are omnivorous, eating both plants and small animals. Because they are voracious feeders on mosquito larvae, they are used for mosquito control in some parts of the world. They are also used to control weeds in flooded rice fields in Japan.

The basic body form of *Triops* has changed very little in hundreds of millions of years. Because many fossil Tadpole Shrimp look quite similar to living *Triops*, the modern species are sometimes known as living fossils. During their long evolutionary history, however, many species of *Triops* have diversified in different parts of the world. As the basic body form is well adapted to their lifestyle, there is little selection for morphological change, but they are diverse in other aspects. In some species, all individuals are female, and eggs develop without the need of fertilization by males. In other species, individuals are hermaphrodites, producing both eggs and sperm, so they are capable of producing offspring by self-fertilization. Still other species have separate males and females and reproduce sexually.

The last vernal pool crustaceans I'll mention are Clam Shrimp. When you first see a Clam Shrimp, you may think you are looking at a swimming clam. Clam Shrimp have two shells like a clam, which help protect the shrimplike animal inside from aquatic predators. They open their shells and extend antennae that they use like oars for swimming. They swim around vernal pools with the hinge of the two shells pointed up, so that the swimming antennae extend beneath. The appearance is that of a clam swimming gracefully through the water column.

Look closely at the life in a temporary pool, and you are likely to discover a world of fascinating animals that you may never have previously encountered. To many people, these bizarre crustaceans look like animals from another era.

9

The Fascinating Flora of Vernal Pools

⅄ Blue Mud Plantain growing over the surface of a vernal pool, in late spring on the Double Helix Ranch.

Vernal pools can form in depressions of bare rock, and many people enjoy hiking to the top of Enchanted Rock in Llano County to see the pools there. Vernal pools also form in low areas of many fields and pastures. The rolling terrain of the Hill Country provides perfect depressions for vernal pools to form after heavy rains. When they fill, it does not take long for the pools to spring to life with a wide diversity of plants and animals.

Among the native plants you are likely to see in and around a vernal pool are several lineages that branched off from other vascular plants before the evolution of seeds. These plants, which include spikemosses, quillworts, horsetails, and ferns, reproduce from spores rather than seeds.

Today, our local descendants of these spore-bearing plant lineages are all quite small and are mostly limited to seasonally wet areas. But about 300 million years ago, some parts of Texas were covered in wet forests and swamps full of the giant, now extinct, relatives of these spore-bearing plants. Most of today's coal deposits around the world are the ancient remains of similar forests. In San Saba County, near the northern edge of the Hill Country, you can see the fossilized evidence of these forests in some of the locally quarried sandstones.

When selecting the material for building our ranch houses, I picked a local sandstone that is full of fossils of extinct clubmosses, horsetails, and tree ferns. As the houses were being built, I remarked to our contractor on the beauty of these fossils and how they reflected the many changes that had occurred over geological time in central Texas. The contractor replied, "Yeah, those fossils must be thousands of years old." When I explained that they are actually about 300 million years old, he said, "Wow, if the quarry had known that, I bet they would have charged you a lot more for this rock!" I smiled and decided to leave the geology lesson for another day.

Although central Texas was long ago covered in forests dominated by ferns, only about eight or so species of ferns are commonly seen in our area today. Two of these are aquatic, and you are likely to find them growing in vernal pools. Neither species looks like a typical fern, however, and many people are surprised to learn that they are ferns. One, known as Waterclover, looks superficially like a four-leaf clover, with leaves that often float on the water's surface. You'll have to look hard to see the other one, Pillwort, which has leaves that look like tiny hairs growing beneath the surface of the water. The vernal pools of Enchanted Rock are a great place to observe this odd fern.

Our other spore-bearing plants also tend to be found in seasonally wet places. Horsetails, or Scouring Rushes, are jointed, cylindrical plants with cones at the top. They were named Scouring Rushes by settlers who used the coarse, silica-containing stems to scour pots and pans clean. Quillworts are yet another common spore-producing group of plants in our area. They are named for their long linear leaves, which resemble the quills on bird feathers.

Vernal pools are also home to numerous groups of seed plants. Around the edges of the pools, you will likely find a vast diversity of sedges. If you are patient and have a good plant guide, you can identify seemingly endless numbers of sedges in the genus *Carex* or in other genera, such as flat sedges, spikerushes, fimbry sedges, and bulrushes. Many people confuse sedges with the superficially similar rushes, which make up a separate family. If you can find the fruits of these plants, you can easily distinguish members of the sedge family (which have one-seeded fruits) from those of the rush family (which have many-seeded fruit capsules). I often hear people use the mnemonic "sedges have edges, and rushes are round," with respect to the stems of the plants, to distinguish sedges from rushes. However, although this will identify some groups of sedges with distinct edges on their stems (such as the *Carex* species), a number of sedge species do in fact have round stems.

Tiny flowering plants known as duckweed may be found floating on the water's surface. Although the plants can flower for sexual reproduction, the flowers are so minute that they are rarely seen by anyone except the most careful observers. Most duckweed reproduction is asexual, however, and the plant can replicate by division at astonishing rates. Duckweed is an important waterfowl food; it can also be used in wastewater treatment or harvested to make a high-protein livestock feed.

Another prominent group of plants with leaves on the water's surface are pondweeds. Unlike free-floating duckweed, however, the several species of pondweed are rooted in the pond's bottom. One of the most common Hill Country species is Diverse-leaf Pondweed; its growth form underwater is very different from its form on the water's surface. When pools first fill in the winter, you are likely to see its light green growth, with its tiny leaves, rising toward the water's surface. Once it reaches the surface in the spring, it puts out much larger, darker green leaves that float across the surface of the pool.

Smartweed is another flowering plant that prefers to grow in shallow water or along the shores of vernal pools. The various species of smartweed have rather small pink or white flowers, but they produce heavy crops of relatively large seeds. When I showed this plant to a group of my students, one of them asked me why it is called smartweed, and I had to look it up. The Oxford English Dictionary quoted an explanation from 1617, when related plants were known as Arsesmart, "because if it touch the taile or other bare skinne, it maketh it smart." In other words, "smart" refers to the sharp pain experienced if one makes the unfortunate mistake of using this plant as an emergency toilet paper substitute.

I'm always happy to see the various species of pondweed, smartweed, and large-seeded grasses (like Eastern Gamagrass) flourishing in our wetlands, in part because the seeds of these plants are favorite foods of waterfowl. The plants' heavy growth through the spring and summer means that the wetlands will be full of attractive food for ducks and other waterfowl when the vernal pools fill in the winter. Positioned as we are toward the southern end of the Central Flyway, most species of migrating wildfowl will stop in, at least for a rest, when there is adequate food and water present.

Several aquatic plants of vernal pools also produce beautiful flowers. One of the most prominent Hill Country species is Creeping Water Primrose, although it tends to favor more continuously wet ponds and wetlands. Its bright yellow flowers and dark green leaves grow along shores and across the surface of ponds and waterways. In areas wetter than central Texas, it can become a serious aquatic pest, as it can cover open water and restrict water flow and access. But in the Hill Country it rarely grows dense enough to create problems.

Another beautiful, and usually much less abundant, flowering plant of our vernal pools is Blue Mud Plantain. This is a native plant of the water hyacinth family. Locally, it grows in shallow vernal pools less than a few inches deep. It has a beautiful blue flower, but you will need to look for it in the morning, as the flowers usually wither by noon. This is another important food for waterfowl, which gave rise to another of its common names, ducksalad.

You may remember that, as a child, you were probably attracted to almost any pool of water. Arm yourself with a set of good field guides or a camera, and you may rediscover the joy of exploring the diversity and beauty of vernal pools as an adult.

10

Those Who Live in Glass Houses

⚡ A pair of diatoms (*Cyclotella* cf. *meneghiniana*). Although this species is generally considered to be part of the plankton of large water bodies, a complex of distinct strains is common in small Hill Country streams. Each specimen is about 6 microns in diameter. *Photo courtesy of Tahmineh Rouzbahani and Edward Theriot.*

Diatoms are among the most important organisms in the world that you probably never think about. Scientists estimate that up to half of the oxygen in the Earth's atmosphere was produced over many millions of years by oceanic and freshwater diatoms. Yes, you can thank the trees and other land plants for some of the oxygen we breathe, but it is really diatoms and other tiny aquatic photosynthesizers that generated much of it.

Diatoms are single-celled algae (aquatic photosynthetic organisms) that live in glass shells. More precisely, the cell walls of diatoms are made of clear, hydrated silicon dioxide. Each diatom has two shells, called frustules, that fit together like the Petri plates that are used to culture bacteria. Hence, one frustule is smaller, and nests inside the larger frustule, just as one Petri plate nests inside the other.

My first serious introduction to diatoms was as an undergraduate. I developed a research project to compare the tadpoles of two closely related species of leopard frogs, and I had determined that the two species preferred different habitats (streams in one case, ponds in the other). I wondered if this might result in their tadpoles eating different diets, so I examined the gut contents of the two species under a microscope.

What I saw were multitudes of geometric shapes that appeared to be tiny glass containers—circles, squares, triangles, rods, and even stars. That is essentially what they were. The silicon dioxide frustules of diatoms are made from the same primary component as glass, and like glass, they are clear and brittle. The tadpole guts were crammed with the remains of diatoms.

Diatoms usually reproduce asexually. When they do, they split their frustules into two parts, and a new frustule grows inside each of the old frustules. The larger of the two frustules produces an offspring the same size as the parent, but the smaller frustule produces a smaller offspring, as the new frustule fits within the smaller half.

If diatoms could only reproduce by asexual division, then the average size of diatoms would grow smaller each generation, as smaller and smaller frustules would have to grow inside the old frustules. To prevent this from happening, eventually the diatoms must reproduce sexually. Male and female gametes are produced, and they fuse to form a zygote. The zygote then grows into a large sphere. A new diatom of maximum size forms within this sphere, and the process of asexual reproduction by division begins anew.

When diatoms die, their bodies fall to the bottom of the body of water where they lived and accumulate there. In parts of the oceans, diatom shells may pile up half a mile deep! These deposits are of great benefit to humans, who use the resulting diatomaceous earth for a multitude of purposes. The tiny glass shells are perfect for polishing surfaces, filtering liquids, making cement, and creating porous ceramics, among many other industrial applications. Diatomaceous earth is also used in organic pest control and as an additive to improve the physical and chemical composition of soil.

New and developing uses of the intricate shells of diatoms include various applications in nanotechnology (building devices at very small scales). The shells of diatoms are useful for producing tiny optical devices as well as for building vehicles for drug delivery to specific parts of the human body.

The oceans are filled with diatoms and other photosynthetic algae (together known as phytoplankton). Phytoplankton account for most of the primary organic production in the world. In addition to silicon shells, the carbon compounds produced by phytoplankton accumulate as vast quantities of organic matter on the floors of the oceans. Over time, these deposits become the primary source for the Earth's vast petroleum reserves. One major type of fossil fuel—coal—is largely formed from deposits of land plants, but our oil and gas reserves are mostly formed from the remains of countless phytoplankton, including diatoms.

The next time you fill up your car at the gas station, remember that every gallon of gasoline represents the ancient remains of billions of tiny diatoms and other phytoplankton. And every time you take a breath, you can thank diatoms for producing much of the oxygen that we all need to live. Who knew that such tiny algae living in glass houses could be so important in our daily lives?

11

A Season of Symphonies

ʎ A chorus of Rio Grande Leopard Frogs in a pond on the Double Helix Ranch.

Texas is famous for its live music venues, but away from the cities and towns, there is a musical opportunity unlike any you may have experienced. The theater I have in mind charges no admission fees. Scheduling is sporadic, and the performers can be picky about showing up if the weather is not to their liking. But if you pick your nights carefully, you will be surrounded by singers who will imprint their songs on your mind and soul, and you will hear a chorus that you will never forget.

Rather than a ticket, you will need a flashlight and boots, or some shoes that you don't mind getting wet. You will also need a bit of patience, because these performers can be a bit shy about singing in front of strangers. Pick a warm, wet, spring night, and head out to a pond or stream where a frog chorus is in progress. As you approach, the chorus will likely pause or stop. But turn off your light, be still and quiet, and soon the calls will start up again.

Different species of frogs and toads each have distinctive calls. The males make the calls to attract females of their own species. Many different species of frogs may be calling simultaneously around a pond, and the females use the calls to select an appropriate mate. Female frogs not only distinguish the calls of males of their own species but can also judge the size of the calling male by the frequency of his call. In general, female frogs prefer the larger, older frogs in a chorus as mates. These males have survived the longest, and so they are likely to be among the best prospects as potential fathers for the hundreds to thousands of offspring that the pair is about to produce.

There are 17 species of frogs that live on the Edwards Plateau. Unfortunately, populations of most frogs and toads have declined precipitously over the past several decades, so a few of these species have become rare in the Hill Country in recent years. Nonetheless, with a little effort and patience, you can hear live performances from a dozen or so species in good frog habitat in the region.

The earliest frogs to sing in the Hill Country are Strecker's Chorus Frogs, which brave the cold of winter to sing their cheerful songs in hopes of attracting mates. Even in the dry winters that are typical of La Niña years, the rain that fills streams and ponds is usually enough to attract choruses of this species. Their loud "Peep! Peep! Peep!" is distinctive and familiar to anyone who goes out wandering along waterways on moist winter days (and especially nights). Another related species, the Spotted Chorus Frog, will soon follow. These frogs prefer smaller puddles in flooded fields, and their calls sound like someone rubbing the tines of a comb—a rapid series of clicks, gradually increasing in frequency.

In late February, if the rains come and the nights are warm, the chorus frogs are joined by various toads. The Hill Country is home to five species of true toads—the Gulf Coast Toad, Woodhouse's Toad, Green Toad, Red-spotted Toad, and Texas Toad. The Texas Toad has been designated the Texas State Amphibian; it was once among the most abundant toads in parts of the Edwards Plateau. Sadly, Texas Toads have disappeared from eastern parts of the Plateau in recent years, likely victims of imported fire ants and overuse of pesticides. The other species of toads are hanging on, although all with greatly reduced populations.

When Ann and I first bought the Double Helix Ranch, our boys Jonathan and Erec were 5 and 8 years old. One day we stopped by a stream and found thousands of Woodhouse's Toads transforming from tadpoles into tiny toadlets. Jonathan and Erec began building little toad houses in the mud along the creek, to give shelter to the toads on a sunny late spring day. Soon, these turned into toad castles. The boys had so much fun that they did not leave the stream for the rest of the day. Sadly, an opportunity to see huge numbers of transforming toads is far less common today than it was then.

Where Woodhouse's Toads remain in the Texas Hill Country, they are among the first toads to call in the spring. They have a long, bleating call that sounds a bit like the "baaaa!" of a sheep. The other toads of the Hill Country have more musical, trilling calls, which differ from one another in the pitch and frequency of their notes. With the decline in Woodhouse's Toads and Texas Toads, the most familiar toad across most of the Hill Country these days is the Gulf Coast Toad. These toads sing their rattling trills during and after wet weather from late spring through summer and into early fall. The smaller Green Toads and Red-spotted Toads are still found in suitable habitat, and both have high-frequency trills that match their smaller body sizes. Both call after heavy late spring and early summer rains.

Spadefoot toads are members of a different family, and they spend most of their lives buried underground. They can stay buried for many months or sometimes even years, so they are well adapted to endure prolonged droughts. They get their name from the spade-shaped ridge on their feet, which they use to dig backward into the soil. Our most common species of spadefoot in the Hill Country is Couch's Spadefoot. The species' calls, made in choruses after heavy rains, are not very musical. A chorus of spadefoot toads sounds like a group of fraternity brothers throwing up after a night of too much drinking.

The largest of our frogs are the so-called true frogs, which are also our most aquatic species. These are the larger frogs that you are likely to see leap into the water when you walk along the bank of a stream or pond. The smaller of our two true frogs is the Rio Grande Leopard Frog, which can be recognized by the distinctive spots on its back that give it its name. The species has a complex call that sounds a bit like chuckling laughter. Its larger relative, the American Bullfrog, gets its name from a call that sounds to some like the bellow of a bull.

One of our smallest species of frogs is among our most commonly seen species—the nearly ubiquitous Blanchard's Cricket Frog. These tiny frogs make a clicking call that sounds like someone rapidly striking two small stones together. Cricket frogs call in the warmer parts of the year, producing a familiar sound from the shores of ponds and streams throughout the spring and summer. As you walk along the shore of most Hill Country streams and ponds, you are likely to see cricket frogs leap into the water in front of you. That's why we named our Golden Retriever "Acris" (the genus name of cricket frogs)—she would always leap into every body of water we encountered.

Another tiny amphibian of Hill Country grasslands is one of our most unusual looking frogs, the Great Plains Narrow-mouthed Toad. It spends much of its life underground, emerging after heavy rains to call in flooded fields and ponds. It has a tiny, pointed head with a very small mouth, but the mouth is nonetheless large enough to feed on ants and termites. The Narrow-mouthed Toad's call is a long, high-pitched bleat.

Great Plains Narrow-mouthed Toads often live in the burrows of tarantulas, in a fascinating mutualistic relationship. The tarantulas provide some protection against predators, and the little toads keep the tarantula's burrow clear of bothersome ants. Often, when I uncover one of these toads in a tarantula burrow, it will seek protection under the large spider. The spider will raise its body as the toad scurries underneath. Although tarantulas often eat frog-sized prey, they don't attack the little Narrow-mouthed Toads that keep their burrows free of ants.

In the canyonlands and limestone outcrops, especially along the southern border of the Edwards Plateau, you will hear two species that belong to a group of mostly tropical frogs. These are both direct developers, meaning that they bypass an aquatic larval stage and develop from eggs directly into miniature frogs. A small species, the Cliff Chirping Frog, is abundant in many areas and has a high-pitched chirp for a call. The other species, the Barking Frog, is much larger, and its loud booming barks often confuse people as to what could be making such a sound. Locals often attribute the Barking Frog's calls to various lizards, because that is what they see when they investigate the cliff by day. The Barking Frogs usually remain well hidden, except to those who are brave enough to follow the calls with a flashlight after dark. When they do, they are rewarded with a view of one of the most magnificent and rarely seen frogs of the Hill Country.

The final frog that you are likely to hear across much of the Edwards Plateau is Cope's Gray Treefrog. These beautiful amphibian jewels spend much of their time in trees and grapevine tangles, where they are masters of camouflage. They change their color between green and gray, and their mottling looks very much like the lichens that cover most of our trees. They sing a short musical trill in the late spring and early summer, and they may continue singing from trees on wet nights even after the mating season has ended.

Spend an evening with a frog chorus, and you will be surprised at how entertained you will be. A good frog chorus is a delight to the ears, but it is also fun to watch the frogs call, with their inflated vocal sacs, and to see the females make their choices of mates. Everyone should experience a frog chorus symphony at least once. It will leave you with smiles and lasting memories.

12

What Happened to All Our Frogs?

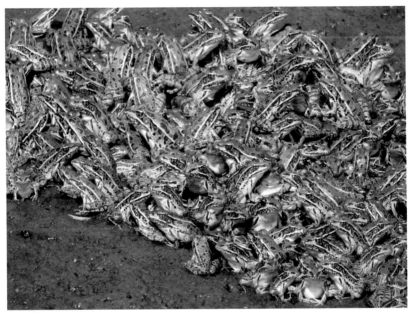

Ʌ A congregation of Rio Grande Leopard Frogs in a drying pond after a boom year.
Sights like this were once much more common in the Hill Country than they are today.

One of my ranch neighbors, Robin Lee, grew up in the Hill Country and spent most of his summers working and playing on his family's ranch. Robin left the area for university and his career but returned in recent years and now manages that ranch. He recently asked me, "What happened to all our frogs?" When I probed him for the basis of his question, he explained. "When I was a teenager, there were frogs and toads everywhere. If we went fishing, we could pick up a bucket of frogs any time with little effort. There were always frogs and toads hopping around everywhere after a rainstorm. I would love to listen to the frogs calling in choruses in the spring. Now, I rarely see or hear any frogs at all. What happened to them?"

Sadly, the decline in frogs and toads is not just a local problem. Amphibian populations have declined or completely disappeared across many areas of the world. In the Hill Country, some species appear to have disappeared completely, whereas others are hanging on, but in lower numbers than occurred historically.

There is no single cause for the decline in amphibians. Rather, many different human-induced changes around the world are creating a perfect storm for these animals. Worldwide, habitat loss to development is one of the biggest factors. Many amphibians have specialized habitat requirements. The cutting of tropical rainforests, loss of grasslands to agriculture, and draining of seasonal wetlands have all resulted in extinctions of species and local populations. But habitat loss is not the only factor in the declines, and it clearly doesn't explain the decline of amphibians on Robin Lee's ranch, which has retained seemingly appropriate habitat for them.

Another major factor in amphibian declines is the global spread of diseases. Just as humans are experiencing a pandemic of a new disease that was transferred from other species (COVID-19), so too have pandemics been a problem across many species of amphibians. In particular, a chytrid (a tiny aquatic fungus that infects the skin of amphibians) has caused a pandemic resulting in the decline or loss of thousands of species of frogs, toads, and salamanders across the Earth. In addition, a virus (known as a ranavirus, which just means "frog virus") has spread widely, causing the death of amphibians as well as some species of fish and aquatic reptiles. The combination of the two pathogens has been devastating to many amphibian populations.

Where did these diseases come from, and how do they spread? Several strains of the chytrid fungus appear to have long infected amphibian populations in parts of the world. Some species have evolved partial resistance to these fungi, just as we have evolved resistance to many of the common pathogens that infect human populations. Pathogens are often most virulent (most likely to cause serious disease) when they first enter a new species.

During the last century, worldwide trade in amphibians increased markedly. For example, large numbers of live amphibians are shipped around the world for food (including the American Bullfrog), for biomedical research (especially the African Clawed Frog and the Mexican Axolotl), and for the pet trade (involving hundreds of species). Pathogens have been transported with these amphibians and then introduced into new species, which often have little or no resistance to the diseases. When different strains of a fungus recombine, they can create new strains, which may be especially virulent as they infect their hosts. Infection with either ranavirus or chytrid fungus may reduce the ability of amphibians to fight off other diseases, so the combination of several new diseases circulating around the world at the same time is especially damaging.

As if habitat loss and rampaging amphibian pandemics were not big enough problems, amphibians have faced growing threats from several other sources. Amphibians absorb water through their skin, so they are especially sensitive to many environmental toxins, especially in water. Widely used herbicides (especially atrazine, which is used to prevent the emergence of broadleaf weeds in some agricultural crops and lawns) have become increasingly abundant in water supplies and are now present even in rainfall. These herbicides mimic the reproductive hormones of vertebrates and have been shown to disrupt the development and reproduction of frogs.

Amphibians are not the only major group of animals that are threatened across the world. Declines are well documented among insects, too, and in addition to being important pollinators of crops and wild plants, insects compose most of the diet of amphibians. Humans have also introduced pest insect species, including the imported fire ants that cause us so much pain and grief across the Gulf states, including Texas. In the spring, these introduced ants often congregate around water sources and consume all the emerging frogs and toads as they transform from tadpoles.

Finally, a global increase in the concentration of carbon dioxide in the Earth's atmosphere is making our climate more variable. We are now experiencing record heat waves, unusual cold snaps, increased flooding, and long periods of drought. All of these climatic changes are especially hard on amphibian populations, many of which depend on temporary ponds for their reproduction.

What, if anything, can landowners do to reverse the losses? Some of the problems are beyond our local control and will require global solutions. But if you want to help preserve and possibly recover remaining local amphibian populations, there are things that you can do to help. First, most of our local amphibians breed in seasonal streams and ponds that periodically dry up. The temporary nature of the ponds is important, because permanent ponds build up populations of predators that consume all the amphibian larvae. These seasonal wetlands are critical resources for many species, including many birds and mammals as well as amphibians. Building or preserving fish-free seasonal ponds can benefit many kinds of wildlife.

Second, be especially careful with the use of herbicides and pesticides, particularly in areas where they can drain directly into wetlands. These toxins not only kill and disrupt the development of amphibians and other aquatic wildlife but they are also dangerous to human health and development when they get into our own water supply.

Third, raccoons are major predators of amphibians (as well as many other small vertebrates). Feed intended for deer is boosting raccoon populations. Limiting raccoon access to corn and other deer supplements (through the use of appropriately designed deer feeders) will save on feed expenses and also help struggling populations of frogs, quail, turkeys, and many other species.

Finally, efforts to protect riparian corridors along waterways will help amphibians and lots of other wildlife while also helping to reduce soil erosion and water pollution.

A rocky pool in a seasonal Hill Country Creek. ➤

III

FLOWING WATERS

Aquifers, Caves, Springs, and Rivers

Early European settlers in the Texas Hill Country were attracted by many things: a mild climate, extensive grasslands, plentiful game, timber, easily quarried stone, and—most of all—abundant, clear, clean water. In places, especially along the escarpment of the Edwards Plateau, water literally bursts forth from the Earth in enormous springs. It is no accident that cities like Austin, San Marcos, New Braunfels, San Antonio, and Del Rio formed along the eastern and southern margins of the Edwards Plateau. These cities took advantage of the ample clear water from Barton, San Marcos, Comal, San Antonio, and San Felipe springs.

≺ The Pedernales River, a tributary of the Colorado River system, in western Travis County.

In other places along the escarpment of the plateau, people found that if they dug shallow wells, water would flow on its own to the surface. The water they tapped was under pressure because it was confined below layers of rock that were not easily penetrated by water. The layers of rock that constitute the aquifer, below the confining layers, are like a giant underground sponge that soaks up water. These layers extend to the west and north into the Edwards Plateau, where water enters the rocks through cracks in the ground. Because the aquifer layers to the west and north are at higher elevations, the water at the well sites was under pressure and would flow to the surface. These flowing wells are called artesian wells, after similar ones that were first bored in the Artois region of France in the eighteenth century.

Unfortunately, as more artesian wells were drilled and more water was released from the Edwards Aquifer, the pressure in the aquifer began to drop. As that happened, the flow of the springs and artesian wells began to decrease, and many stopped flowing altogether. Pumps were added to force more water to the surface, and the aquifer continued to decline. Today, the many competing interests vying for the underground water (including cities, farms and ranches, recreational facilities, and aquatic ecosystems) are engaged in numerous court fights and regulation battles.

The water that emerges from the Edwards Plateau is important well beyond the Hill Country. The springs feed into and form the rivers that drain the plateau, including the Colorado, Guadalupe, San Antonio, Medina, Frio, Nueces, and Devils River systems. The western end of the Plateau is defined by the Pecos River, which originates high in the mountains of New Mexico. Most of that mountain water, however, is used by humans long before it reaches Texas. The Pecos is then recharged by enormous springs and spring-fed creeks along the western edge of the Hill Country, such as Independence Creek in Terrell County. The clear, strong waters of the Pecos, as seen in its remote lower canyons, are a stunning surprise to people who are familiar only with the meager, saline flow of water that emerges from New Mexico.

The rivers that flow east and south off the Edwards Plateau deliver freshwater downstream, where they provide drinking and agricultural water to large populations of Texans. These rivers provide critical freshwater to the bay systems along the Texas coast, which are vital for the rich and varied marine life there. The brackish-water bays are essential nurseries for fishes, crabs, shrimp, and other abundant marine life.

Visitors to the Hill Country are often attracted by its clear, spring-fed streams and rivers. People love to swim, float, paddle, fish, and snorkel in the clear water. The clarity of the water allows easy viewing of the abundant aquatic life, much of which is found nowhere else in the world. The rivers wind through beautiful canyons and rock formations as well, allowing views of magnificent ancient rock art—carved or painted by many generations of indigenous human inhabitants. The exposures of rock are also great places to see fossils, from half-billion-year-old Cambrian stromatolites along the Llano and James Rivers to remains of Pleistocene mammoths that shared the Hill Country with humans just a few thousand years ago.

The chapters in this section will explore the life that has evolved in the underground aquifers of the Edwards Plateau, as well as its springs, streams, and river valleys. Beyond the water itself, the riparian corridors along the streams and rivers of the Hill Country provide a home for countless species of plants and animals that cannot exist in the drier environs of the Edwards Plateau.

13

Life without Light

⋏ The Austin Blind Salamander, *Eurycea waterlooensis*, one of the many endemic species of the Edwards Aquifer.

Deep under the Edwards Plateau, from enormous caves to tiny fissures in porous rock, lie giant underground reservoirs of water known as aquifers. The water in these aquifers is actually more like the water in a sponge than an underground lake. The rocks that form an aquifer contain spaces and openings that hold water. The spaces are formed mostly by the action of water dissolving parts of the rock over millions of years. In addition, cracks and faults sometimes allow water to flow and penetrate from one layer of rock to another. Some layers of rock are relatively impervious to water, whereas others are easily dissolved by it. Springs tend to form where a porous, water-filled layer of rock comes into contact with a less permeable layer of rock. Water flows from the saturated strata just as it flows from a saturated sponge sitting on a tabletop. How did these aquifers form in the first place?

Through much of the Cretaceous Period (about 145.5–65.5 million years ago), a vast shallow sea occupied most of the area where the Edwards Plateau is located today. The limestones that were deposited in the bottom of this sea were largely formed from degraded remains of marine life—from microorganisms to giant mollusks, fishes, and marine reptiles. These organisms used calcium carbonate in seawater to create their shells and skeletons, which then broke down and settled to the bottom of the sea as the animals died. Over the millions of years of the Cretaceous, the sediments accumulated to form thick limestone rock.

By the Eocene epoch (55.8–34 million years ago), the Cretaceous seabed had become a low, exposed bank inland from the coastal plain. Through the Eocene, this bank was gradually and slowly uplifted. By the Oligocene (34–23 million years ago), more uplift in the western and northern regions of the exposed bank tilted the deposits toward the Gulf Coast. This tilting increased erosion and water runoff, which began to create deep valleys and rock expo- sures. It was during this time that Edwards limestone deposits were exposed at the surface, and their eroded sediments began to form alluvial deposits on the Gulf coastal plain.

By the end of the Oligocene and into the beginning of the Miocene (23–5.3 million years ago), a period of rapid uplift and faulting occurred. This produced the Balcones Fault Zone, which uplifted the Edwards Plateau and produced its distinctive eastern and southern borders. Uplifting continued through the Miocene and into the Pliocene (5.3–2.6 million years ago), which increased erosion of the Cretaceous deposits. These deposits were thinnest in the center of the Edwards Plateau, where granitic uplifts had occurred long before the Cretaceous seas had formed and covered the area. In parts of this region, the Cretaceous limestones were eroded completely away in the Miocene, thus exposing the much older rocks below. This exposed the Llano Uplift, or the Central Texas Mineral Region, as we know it today.

As the Edwards Plateau formed across many millions of years, it experienced a wide range of climates. At times in the fairly recent past (the last few million years), the Edwards Plateau was a much cooler, wetter place than it is today. Many of the plant and animal groups found today far to the east and north in North America once were common on the Edwards Plateau. As the plateau gradually became drier and hotter, some of those species went extinct. But others found refuge in the cool, wet canyons that formed from erosion on the eastern and southern margin of the plateau. For example, the beautiful Bigtooth Maples of Lost Maples State Park are close relatives of the Sugar Maples found in more eastern and northern forests.

Some aquatic species found refuge deep underground, in the cool waters and caves of the Edwards Aquifer. Several species of catfishes, about a dozen species of salamanders, and hundreds of species of crustaceans, insects, spiders, harvestmen, centipedes, and myriad other small invertebrates moved underground as the surface conditions became inhospitable to their existence.

Life underground is easy in some ways, but it also presents considerable challenges. The primary challenge is the lack of light. Without light, there can be no photosynthesis, so most of the nutrients that are needed for living ecosystems must come from the surface. Today, many of those nutrients are provided by guano from the enormous bat colonies that live in caves of the Edwards Plateau. In addition, remains of plants and animals are carried by water as it flows into the caves and fissures of rock that lead to the underground aquifers.

Those nutrient sources feed bacteria and other microorganisms, which provide food for tiny invertebrate animals, which provide food for larger invertebrates, which provide food for the catfishes and salamanders—the top predators of the underground food pyramid. But the catfishes and salamanders have to catch their prey without the benefit of seeing them, as they live in perpetual darkness. Without selection for sight, the genes that would normally form functional eyes start to accumulate mutations, and over millions of years, the catfishes and salamanders have lost their eyes and thus their ability to see. Even though they are blind, they have enhanced lateral line systems that detect movement, even tiny vibrations, in the water, and enhanced olfactory systems to detect scent. Their exaggerated heads and broad snouts make them uniquely sensitive to the presence of prey nearby.

Some salamanders persisted in the surface springs of the Edwards Plateau as well. They also colonized the underground waters of the Edwards Plateau multiple times. Each time they did so, they faced similar selection pressures. The species that live deep in the aquifers often lose much or all of their skin pigment, as there is no need to protect their bodies from ultraviolet light, and little need for color patterns in a lightless environment. Therefore, many subterranean species are white, pale, or translucent. They also tend to have elongated limbs, which are useful for clinging to rocks deep in the aquifer. Most troglobites (animals that live exclusively underground) lack eyes, but they often have exaggerated features, like the catfishes and salamanders mentioned above, associated with alternative sensory systems. All those changes give them a strange, otherworldly appearance. Biologists, cavers, and nature enthusiasts from throughout the world come to the caves of the Texas Hill Country to see these fascinating underground animals that are endemic to the Edwards Aquifer. All this underground endemism also helps to make the Texas Hill Country a global hot spot for biodiversity.

14

Lanterns of Summer

⋏ Fireflies and stars glowing through a summer night along Independence Creek, at the western end of the Edwards Plateau. *Time-lapse photograph courtesy of Ian M. Wright.*

Adults of a certain age likely remember a childhood filled with fireflies. Called lightning bugs by some, especially in the eastern United States, they are neither flies nor true bugs but rather belong to a family of beetles. In any case, on warm summer nights, many of us filled jars with fireflies collected from around our houses and marveled at their flashing lights. But today, a yard or field full of flashing fireflies is a much rarer sight than it was a half-century ago.

Certain sights, sounds, and scents are touchstones of our youth. A hillside covered with the brilliant flashing lights of thousands of fireflies is one of those for me. It is a sight that always sets my mind swirling with vivid, wonderful memories of summer nights filled with excitement and joy.

Sadly, many of the 2,000 species of fireflies around the world are now in decline. The primary reasons are loss of habitat, light pollution, increased use of insecticides, and, around cities, the use of electric "bug-zappers."

Most species of fireflies prefer wet or at least moist habitats. In the Hill Country, one of the best remaining places to observe fireflies is along the rivers that drain the Edwards Plateau. Fireflies like those wet areas because their larvae, called glowworms, feed on worms, slugs, and snails that require moist habitats. The larvae live mostly in rotting logs and moist soil, where they can stay hydrated and find abundant prey.

Adult fireflies use their lights to attract mates. Different species of fireflies have specific flashing patterns, and different species emit different wavelengths of light. The light can vary from green to yellow to pale red, and under low-light conditions the flashes of some species can appear almost blue.

Two of the most commonly observed groups of fireflies in the United States are members of the genera *Photinus* and *Photuris*. *Photinus* fireflies secrete noxious compounds (called lucibufagins) that help repel most predators. But *Photuris* fireflies cannot produce these compounds themselves, so they resort to trickery to obtain them. Female *Photuris* fireflies mimic the flashes of *Photinus* females and thus draw in *Photinus* males that are looking for a mate. Rather than mating, the *Photuris* females attack and eat the *Photinus* males that they attract, thus obtaining the lucibufagins that they need for their protection.

Firefly flashes are a type of light called bioluminescence. The light is produced by a chemical reaction that combines oxygen with an enzyme known as luciferase. The resulting light production is extremely efficient, as 100 percent of the energy from the reaction is released as light, with no heat production. Contrast that with the efficiency of a typical incandescent lightbulb, which produces only about 5 percent light and 95 percent heat.

The gene that encodes luciferase has been cloned, and it is now commonly used as a signal to report gene activity in experimental biology. The gene is inserted as part of a cluster of genes into certain cells. When the genes are activated, the cells in question will glow and can easily be seen by the experimenter.

Like many insects, fireflies undergo a complete metamorphosis in their life cycle. In the Hill Country, adult fireflies are active mostly in the late spring and early summer. After they have attracted mates with their flashes, the females lay eggs in or on moist soil. The eggs hatch into larvae that also produce light, and thus are called glowworms. In fact, the glowworms of all firefly species produce light, although there are some species of fireflies that do not produce light as adults.

The larvae overwinter (sometimes for several successive years) and then pupate in the spring. The pupal stage lasts from one to a few weeks, during which the glowworm transforms into an adult firefly. The new fireflies then seek out their mates and repeat the cycle, usually living for just a few months.

One of the main reasons for firefly declines is the loss of wetland habitats, since the fireflies need the wet soils and rotting logs for their larvae to flourish. Clearing fallen trees from bottomlands eliminates firefly habitat. Fireflies can thrive in yards and gardens as well, but only if appropriate decaying vegetation is left as part of the habitat.

Even where appropriate habitat persists, fireflies face several other challenges. Outside lights confuse and attract fireflies, preventing them from mating. Worse, electric bug-zappers attract many fireflies to their deaths by electrocution. Most people install bug-zappers to control mosquitos, but mosquitos are not attracted to light, so they are largely ineffective for that purpose. The bug-zappers do attract and kill any passing fireflies, however.

Fireflies are also one of many groups of beneficial insects that are declining as a result of heavy use of insecticides. Decades of widespread insecticide use have resulted in declines in many kinds of insects, including butterflies, the predatory insects that control agricultural pests, and many other insects that serve as a food base for other species or perform important functions such as pollination.

If you would like to help restore firefly populations, consider doing some or all of the following: Leave riparian habitat along creeks and rivers undisturbed, including rotting logs. Reduce outdoor light use, and get rid of ineffective bug-zappers (which mostly kill beneficial insects). Plant native wildflowers in your garden, and minimize or eliminate your use of insecticides (there are many other more effective ways to control most insect pests). These simple changes will allow beneficial insects like fireflies to thrive, and you may once again delight in the nighttime light show of summer.

15

Musings about Mussels

Ʌ A freshwater mussel (*Lampsilis*) with its fishlike lure extended. *Photo courtesy of Chris Barnhart.*

The Llano River was once a famous place for observing and collecting mussels (a family of freshwater clams called unionids by biologists). In the late 1800s and early 1900s, before the advent of plastics, our native freshwater mussel shells were in great demand for use in making buttons for clothing. Small circles were drilled from the mussel shells and fashioned into mother-of-pearl buttons. The market peaked in 1916, when 40 million buttons were produced from mussel shells across the United States.

The button industry was just one of many pressures that freshwater mussels had to endure. Mussels are slow-growing and long-lived—most grow for decades, and some for over a century. They are (or were) critical for water quality, as they constantly filter large quantities of water, purifying it in the process. In addition to demand for their shells by the button industry, mussels were collected for food and by people looking for relatively rare freshwater pearls.

As if collecting did not place enough pressure on mussels, environmental degradation certainly contributed to the decline of our native populations. Heavy overgrazing of the Edwards Plateau led to massive runoff and floods of the Llano River in the early 1900s, with associated siltation and degradation of water quality. Then, about 50 years ago, two species of the Asian clam genus *Corbicula* were introduced into the rivers of Texas, including the Llano River.

The Asian clams reproduced in enormous numbers, and without their normal predators and pathogens, the populations periodically undergo boom and bust cycles. They reproduce rapidly, and they compete with our native mussels for suspended particles of food. Every few years, the clam populations get so large that they starve and then die by the billions. The decaying bodies often result in algal blooms and cloudy water. Many of the long-lived native mussels die as well in these bust events, presumably from the degradation in water quality.

If you look along the shores of the Llano River today, or search the sediments in the river, you will find multitudes of Asian clam shells. But you will see only the occasional native mussel shell these days and find even fewer living native individuals. Sadly, many of the native mussels that persist in the rivers of the Edwards Plateau today are endangered or threatened with extinction.

Our native mussels are much larger than the abundant Asian clams. The Asian clam shells rarely exceed an inch in length, whereas many of our native mussels are the size of a human hand, or even larger. They have wonderful and evocative common names, such as Texas Fatmucket, Texas Heelsplitter, Triangle Pigtoe, Texas Fawnsfoot, and Texas Pimpleback. In recent canoe trips down the Llano, I've observed live individuals of the endangered Texas Fatmucket species, although the famed "mussel shoals" of the Llano are now ancient history.

Our native freshwater mussels have some remarkable ways of reproducing. For example, the Texas Fatmucket uses an extension of its body as a lure to attract predatory fish. The lure looks just like a small bait fish, down to spots that look like eyes and extensions that look like fins. A Fatmucket will extend this lure and vibrate it in a way that looks like a small, swimming fish. Bass are attracted to this mussel lure, just as they would be to a lure used by a fisherman.

Why would a mussel want to attract a bass? When a bass attempts to eat the lure, the mussel has a surprise for the fish. The mussel expels hundreds of tiny offspring, called glochidia, which then clamp onto the gills of the fish. The tiny glochidia then parasitize and live off the fish, until they develop enough size to drop off and live independently.

Other species of freshwater mussels use distinctive lures to attract different host fish species. Some mussels have a lure that resembles a worm, and they entice sunfishes to serve as hosts to their young. Still others have a lure that resembles a crayfish. The evolution of these diverse lures is all the more remarkable when one realizes that the mussels cannot see—and yet they have lures that use visual cues to attract their fish hosts. These mussel lures have evolved to look like bait fish through natural selection. Over time, the mussel lures that are most attractive to the host fish result in the highest levels of mussel reproduction, and the genetic instructions for these successful lures are then passed on to the mussel's offspring through their DNA.

Long-time residents of the Hill Country are likely to remember a time when the water of the Llano River ran much clearer than it does today. There are many reasons for this decline in water quality, including sewage runoff, agricultural runoff, and other sources of pollution. But the loss of the abundant native freshwater mussels, with their ability to serve as efficient water filters, also contributes to the change.

The next time you visit the Llano River or other rivers of the Edwards Plateau for a swim or a float trip, you might try searching the gravel banks for native freshwater mussel shells. For every several thousand Asian clam shells that you see, you might find one native freshwater mussel shell. If you snorkel the river and are lucky, you may even see some live Texas Fatmuckets with their amazing lures extended, trying to fool a fish into hosting the mussel's offspring.

16

The Last Wild River

Ʌ Jonathan in Lewis Canyon on the Lower Pecos River. The author's son scouts some rapids before attempting a run in a canoe.

United States Highway 290 originally followed the old stagecoach route west from Junction, through Sonora and Ozona, across the dry western end of the Edwards Plateau. It then wound down the steep western escarpment of the plateau adjacent to Fort Lancaster, before crossing the Pecos River. Early biologists stayed at Fort Lancaster and collected type specimens of new species in the spring-fed waters of nearby Live Oak Creek and the Pecos River Valley.

Much of Highway 290 was replaced by Interstate 10 decades ago. Today, most travelers take the Interstate, so they do not get to experience the dramatic climb down the western escarpment of the plateau to the Pecos as it was experienced by generations before them. But the next time you are driving west to the Trans-Pecos region, take a little extra time and turn off at the old Highway 290 exit for Fort Lancaster.

Just before you drop off the plateau into the valley of the Pecos, there is a scenic roadside picnic spot. If you pull off there, you will have a commanding view of the Pecos Valley from the edge of the Edwards Plateau. Miles to the west, you will see another, similar plateau, the Stockton Plateau. Geologically, the two plateaus are closely related. Over millions of years, they were separated by the action of the Pecos River as it cut down through the limestone deposited by the ancient Cretaceous sea.

If you continue west down the escarpment, in a few miles you will cross the Pecos River. At this point, the Pecos is little more than a small, muddy, saline creek. From that crossing, it is about 130 miles downstream to the next major bridge over the river, the U.S. Highway 90 high bridge near the Mexican border. In between these bridges is one of the most remote and wildest rivers left in the United States, and certainly in Texas.

The western escarpment of the Edwards Plateau and the eastern escarpment of the Stockton Plateau quickly converge on the riverbanks about 30 miles south of the Highway 290 crossing. At about the same point, enormous freshwater springs, beginning at Independence Creek, recharge the saline Pecos. For its last 100 miles, the Pecos is transformed into a clear, wild, fast-flowing river, running through deep canyons that are filled with rapids, rock shelters, ancient rock art, wildlife, and a fascinating mix of eastern and western plants and animals.

The first time I canoed down the 130-mile stretch of the Lower Pecos was in 1979, when I was hired to conduct a survey of the amphibians, reptiles, and fishes of the remote river canyons. Unlike most of the other rivers of the Edwards Plateau, this part of the Pecos is remote and difficult, so much so that few people attempt this particular float trip. Most of those who do usually begin their trip about halfway down, at the only other public access point— what was for many years a low-water crossing on the dirt road that runs through the tiny town of Pandale (there is now a new bridge at this location).

ʌ Rock art in a shelter along the Pecos River.

A canoe trip down the Pecos is not a weekend affair. On our 1979 trip, we traveled two weeks down the river, from the Highway 290 crossing near Fort Lancaster to the Lake Amistad boat ramp near the Mexican border, taking time to explore and sample biological specimens along the way. A trip down the Lower Pecos takes considerable planning, preparation, effort, and, above all, endurance. The river conditions are usually best in the May rainy season, but that is also when the river is most likely to flood. When the river rises, the confines of the steep canyon walls can make for very dangerous conditions. There is no cell service, there are very few roads anywhere near the river, and it is a long hike out to find any help. Paddlers must carry food, drinking water, first-aid supplies, and camping gear, all of which may be lost from swamped canoes in violent rapids. Several of the larger rapids can be dangerous, especially for an open-top canoe. I've broken bones (fortunately, just ribs and coccyx) on two trips down the Pecos, and there is little one can do about injuries except tough them out. Remains of canoes wrapped around rocks or buried in gravel are

∧ Rock carvings at Lewis Canyon on the Pecos River.

about the only thing left of many ill-fated canoe trips down the Lower Pecos canyons.

On the other hand, the rapids, canyons, and scenery could not be more beautiful. I've returned to make a trip down the Lower Pecos at least once every decade since my first experience in the 1970s. The stunning ancient rock paintings in rock shelters and carvings on river overlooks never cease to amaze and inspire me. Every trip, I discover new rock art and see species of plants and animals that I've never seen before. Rarely have I ever seen another human on my trips down the Pecos who was not part of my travel party. I can vividly recall every day and night that I've spent on this river, and every one of them was spectacular.

For years, I missed seeing a particular ancient rock painting known as the Electric Shaman, which is painted on the roof of a rock shelter. I read about it, and looked for it, but somehow it kept eluding me over a dozen or so trips. My son Jonathan joined me and two friends on my most recent trip down the Pecos, and I told him as we launched that it was our mission to find it at last.

Λ The Electric Shaman.

Late one day on the river, a violent thunderstorm began to build. This is a sign to seek shelter fast, not only because of the danger of lightning but also because the river can rise quickly and escape routes out of the canyons are limited. After considerable effort, we finally found a narrow access to a rock shelter above the river; as the skies turned dark, we made camp there. We were well protected during an extremely active and noisy thunderstorm that night, and from the protection of the rock shelter, we marveled and sipped some welcome bourbon as the lightning lit up the cliffs along the river.

The next morning, as I started making breakfast in the rock shelter, Jonathan was still lying in his sleeping bag, looking up at the stone ceiling. As morning began to light up the canyon, suddenly he exclaimed, "Dad, there it is! The Electric Shaman!" Sure enough, it had been staring down at us all night, through the lightning storm. It was the face of a shaman with hair standing straight up, as if he had been hit by lightning. I wondered if it had been storms like the one we had just experienced that inspired this particular painting so many centuries ago.

Back home in Austin, writing and thinking about the Electric Shaman makes me want to visit him again, there in his protected rock shelter, where he patiently guards the western edge of the Edwards Plateau through the millennia. I hope that he stays there, protected and unmolested, for many millennia more.

IV

LIFE OF A GRASSLAND

As the early European settlers in Texas crossed the Edwards Plateau from south to north or east to west, they encountered large stretches of grasslands between the wooded hills and canyons. These grasslands are the southern end of the Great Plains of North America, and many common prairie species of plants and animals have their southernmost distribution on the Edwards Plateau. This patchwork of woodlands, wet canyons, and grasslands creates a mosaic that helps make the Edwards Plateau such a diverse place. Here, east meets west, and north meets south, leading to some unexpected juxtapositions of plants and animals.

Although grasslands are defined and dominated by grasses, they are also home to abundant species of

≺ Lazy Daisies in a grassy meadow on the Double Helix Ranch.

broad-leaved flowering plants (forbs), as well as numerous animals that eat the plants and their seeds. Grasslands are extremely productive ecosystems, as much of the vegetation is produced and consumed every year. Herds of large grazing mammals like bison, as well as abundant rodents and insects, make grasslands their home. The rodents and insects, in turn, attract many species of grassland birds and snakes.

Today, grasslands are among the ecosystems that are most in peril across the Edwards Plateau. Early European settlers tended to overstock the ranges, and overgrazing was common. Without the cover of grasses, heavy rains washed away topsoil in some places, leaving exposed rock or caliche. Once the topsoil has washed away, recovery of the grasslands is very slow. Fortunately, enough natural vegetation remained in most places to hold soils in place, even when many of the native grasses were eliminated.

A second threat came to the grasslands as settlers attempted to "improve" them by planting fast-growing grasses from other places (including Europe, Asia, South America, and Africa). Unfortunately, these nonnative grasses do little to support the native animals of the Edwards Plateau, and most of them require large inputs of expensive fertilizers and extensive irrigation to maintain their fast growth rates. Many ranchers now realize that the benefits of native grasses include their ability to withstand the extreme droughts of the Edwards Plateau and their ability to flourish without supplemental fertilization or irrigation. They also support native game species and other wildlife, which now bring in far more income than do livestock for most ranchers.

Now many ranchers and other landowners are working to restore the native grasslands to their former glory. Appropriately restored and managed native grasslands will support more livestock, as well as far more native species of plants and animals, compared with so-called "improved" pastures of planted, nonnative grasses. Restoration of these grasslands is not as simple as throwing some seeds on the ground, however. The chapters of this section will introduce the biology and diversity of native grasses while discussing the goals, methods, and complexities of grassland restoration.

17

Why Do Some Grasses Grow in the Winter, But Others in the Summer?

⋏ Texas Bluegrass (*Poa arachnifera*), a cool-season C3 grass.

W hen I hike around the Double Helix Ranch after a period of summer rains, I can't help but admire the fresh green growth of some of our warm-season grasses. In wet and warm conditions, Indiangrass, Big Bluestem, Little Bluestem, Switchgrass, Sideoats Grama, Hairy Grama, Silver Bluestem, Sand Dropseed, Arizona Cottontop, Carolina Jointstem, Eastern Gamagrass, the perennial lovegrasses, and many other native grasses put up vigorous new leaves among the dried dead ones they produced the previous year. Even when summer rains are not substantial, these perennial grasses are able to put on new growth because they have deep root systems that tap the moisture far underground. They also have some special adaptations that allow them to grow well on our long, hot summer days.

In the winter, you will see the cool-season grasses—such as Texas Wintergrass (also called Speargrass), Texas Bluegrass, Great Plains Wildrye, Six-Weeks Fescue, and Heller's Rosettegrass—as bright green patches in otherwise brown pastures of last year's warm-season grasses. Many of these cool-season grasses grow best under and around oak trees in the Hill Country. But why do these grasses grow in the winter, and die back in the summer, whereas our warm-season grasses do just the opposite?

Plants grow by using energy from sunlight to convert water and carbon dioxide into sugars that they use for growth, with oxygen as a by-product. This is the process we call photosynthesis. The oxygen that plants produce in photosynthesis is the oxygen that we breathe every day.

The cool-season grasses use a type of photosynthesis that is common to most plants. The first step produces a three-carbon molecule, so we call this "C3 photosynthesis," and the plants that use this process are called "C3 plants." C3 photosynthesis works well as long as moisture is abundant and temperatures are relatively cool, but under conditions of lots of sunlight, high temperatures, and water stress, C3 plants struggle. Under those conditions, one of the enzymes involved in photosynthesis binds with oxygen and greatly reduces the efficiency of photosynthesis, as well as water use by the plant. This is why many of the plants in your vegetable garden grow well through the early spring but die back in the heat of summer, even if you water them.

In contrast, many plants native to hot climates have evolved another form of photosynthesis, called C4 photosynthesis. As you might expect, these plants produce a four-carbon compound early in photosynthesis. The four-carbon compound transfers and concentrates carbon dioxide around the photosynthetic enzyme, which keeps it from binding to oxygen instead. This greatly improves the efficiency of photosynthesis as well as water use by the plant.

So why don't all plants use the more efficient C4 photosynthesis? The changes needed for C4 photosynthesis entail some costs to the plant, so it is advantageous only when temperatures and sunlight are high and available moisture is relatively low. Because the Hill Country is hot and dry through most summers, most of our native grasses are C4 grasses. The C3 grasses simply can't tolerate our heat and frequent drought conditions in summer.

Many of our C3 grasses are annuals that seed out and spend the summer resting as seeds. Others, such as Texas Bluegrass and Texas Wintergrass, are perennials that die back to the ground in the summer, letting the roots rest underground through the hot months. They then put out new growth when cooler and wetter conditions return in the late fall or winter. Texas Bluegrass—an extremely valuable, beautiful, and beneficial native cool-season grass of the Hill Country—provides grazers high-quality forage in the winter. It is more common in the Hill Country than in many other parts of its native range, but sadly it has disappeared from many pastures because of overgrazing. If you have good stands of Texas Bluegrass in your pastures in the winter and early spring, that is a great sign of excellent management.

Having a good mix of cool-season and warm-season grasses is a key to quality grasslands, as it makes fresh green growth of grasses available to grazers nearly year-round. In general, most of our native grasses are C4, warm-season grasses, although all of the cool-season grasses I mentioned above are native. C3 grasses tend to be more common at high latitudes, where it may be cool and wet enough for them to thrive in the summer. Some of these C3 grasses have been introduced to Texas, where they grow mostly in the winter. Many of these compete with our native plants and may inhibit spring growth of more desirable species. Japanese Brome, Rescuegrass, and Winter Ryegrass are all examples of invasive cool-season C3 grasses. They provide some limited late winter grazing, but they end up displacing some of our more valuable and useful native grasses.

Healthy native grasslands require little maintenance, providing both livestock and wildlife with appropriate food and cover throughout the year. Native grasses are also beautiful in their own right. The more you know about them and how they live, the more you may come to respect and enjoy the diversity, resilience, and beauty of our native flora.

18

Butterflies, Hummingbirds, and Other Pollinators

⋀ A blue Dayflower (*left*) and a field of red Standing Cypress (*right*). Can you guess what animals are most likely to pollinate each?

When most people think of nectar feeders, hummingbirds immediately come to mind. Many other animal groups—such as butterflies, moths, bees, and even some bats—also feed on the nectar produced by flowers. There is a significant energetic cost to the plants in producing this nectar, so why do they do it? The nectar attracts the animals to feed, and in feeding on the nectar from one flower to the next, these animals transfer pollen between the flowers. This transfer of pollen allows static plants to reproduce with other members of their own species. Nectar is just the plants' way of inducing animals to assist plants in having sex with other plants.

Since many plants depend on pollinators to carry their pollen to other flowers, they provide the nectar in structures that are accessible only to these pollinators. In feeding, the pollinator must brush against the pollen-bearing structures of the plants so that the animals pick up some of the sticky pollen and carry it to the next flower. Thus, the nectar-bearing structures of plants have coevolved with specialized feeding structures of their pollinators, which ensures that the valuable nectar will be used by the animals that are most likely to pollinate the plants successfully. Different species of plants tend to attract different kinds of pollinators, which is the main reason that flowers of different species of plants have such a wide diversity of colors, shapes, and scents.

Plants that are specialized to attract hummingbird pollinators usually have long, tubular flowers, and most of those flowers are red. Hummingbirds are highly attracted to the color red, although they are also attracted by some other bright colors, including orange, pink, and purple.

Hummingbirds have a long, specialized tongue that coils up inside the bird's head when retracted. The retracted tongue may actually wrap around the skull and eyes inside the head, and then it can be extruded far beyond the tip of a hummingbird's long pointed beak. When a hummingbird feeds, it extends its tongue deep into a tubular flower (or a feeder). The tip of the tongue is forked, and the sides of the tongue roll up to produce two tubelike structures to hold the nectar.

Biologists once thought that hummingbirds used their tubular tongues like a straw, to suck up nectar; however, recent high-speed videos of hummingbirds feeding show that is not the case. Instead, the hummingbird flattens the tubes of its tongue as it approaches a flower, then opens up the tubes as the tip of the tongue encounters nectar. The tongue acts like a pump that fills with nectar, which is then withdrawn into the bird's mouth and emptied. A humming-bird fills and empties its tongue in this way about 15 to 20 times a second!

You can usually guess what animal pollinates a given species of flowering plant by examining the structure and color of the flower. Some insects (such as butterflies and moths) also have long tongues that can be extended into tubular flowers. Because most butterflies and hummingbirds tend to be attracted to similar colors (yellow, orange, pink, purple, and red), many of the plants that are attractive to hummingbirds are also attractive to butterflies. Most moths are active at night, and with little light, the most visible flowers are white. So, plants that are pollinated by moths and other nocturnal animals are often white.

Neither hummingbirds nor butterflies are especially attracted to blue flowers, so what is pollinating blue flowers like our showy Texas Bluebonnets or Dayflowers? Any color on the blue to purple spectrum is quite attractive to bees, and most blue flowers are bee-pollinated. Bees are also attracted to yellow. You may have noticed that most early spring flowers are yellow or blue, and then red and orange flowers appear later in the spring, when butterflies and hummingbirds are more likely to be present. If you look closely at bees visiting flowers, you will see that in addition to nectar, many bees also gather pollen, which you can see as bright yellow packets on their legs.

What we see when we look at a flower, however, is not necessarily what many insects are seeing. That is because most insects can detect light in the ultraviolet spectrum, which is invisible to our eyes. Many flowers that look plain to us can have vivid patterns in the ultraviolet spectrum, patterns that are used to attract pollinators and guide them to the nectar reward.

If you would like to attract hummingbirds and butterflies to your ranch or yard, there are numerous native wildflowers that are easy to grow from seed and highly attractive to pollinators. In the chapter on hummingbirds, I mention one of these—the beautiful and elegant Standing Cypress with its array of bright red tubular flowers. Several other popular native wildflowers produce abundant nectar and have flowers that attract hummers and butterflies. The various species of mints of the genus *Monarda*, such as Lemon Mint, Spotted Beebalm, and Basil Beebalm, also produce showy late spring flowers that are loved by hummingbirds and butterflies. Later in the spring and early summer, American Basketflower produces beautiful and interesting pink flowers, and as a bonus, its seeds are relished by the Northern Bobwhite and other birds. During the fall migrations of butterflies and hummingbirds, the purple spikes of Gayfeather are important and attractive to these pollinators. The yellow flowers of Cowpen Daisy are not very attractive to hummers, but they are loved by many butterflies, such as our beautiful Monarchs as they fly through in the fall on their way to their overwintering grounds in Mexico. With a little planning, you can have attractive and showy flowers that will attract hummers and butterflies from March through late fall, and you can enjoy the beauty and diversity of both the flowers and their animal pollinators.

19

The Noble Life of a Dung-Roller

⋀ A large mass of dung beetles competing for a heap of cattle dung.

It takes a special kind of person to see beauty in a dung beetle—but what magnificent creatures they are! You have probably seen dung beetles rolling balls of dung across a pasture, often with one dung beetle riding on the ball as it is rolled along by another. What are these insects, and what are they doing with that ball of dung?

Dung beetles are found throughout tropical and temperate parts of the world, on every continent except Antarctica, with about 5,000 species of dung beetles known worldwide. Of those, 58 are known in Texas, and a few dozen species are commonly seen in the Hill Country. The various Texas species range in size from about half an inch to an inch long, and the colors of the adult beetles vary across shades of green, brown, and black.

Both adult and larval dung beetles feed on dung, and they especially like the dung of large herbivores, such as cattle. Some of our dung beetles (known as tunnelers) dig tunnels under dung patties, where they bury the dung and lay their eggs. The dung beetle larvae (grubs) then feed on the dung until they metamorphose into beetles. Other species of dung beetles (dwellers) live and feed inside of dung piles. Still other species (rollers) roll the dung into a ball, move it some distance away from the dung pile, and bury it. The dung-rollers, or tumblebugs, are the dung beetles that you are most likely to have noticed.

A few species of dung beetles found in Texas have been imported and purposefully introduced to the state, as well as to many other places around the world. Why would anyone want to introduce dung beetles? Because they are extremely beneficial insects. A robust population of dung beetles can quickly remove cattle dung and bury it underground. This greatly reduces the possibility that flies and other pests will breed in the dung, and it removes dung before it can wash into surface waters, thereby potentially polluting our water supply. The dung buried by dung beetles also fertilizes and aerates the soil.

A healthy cattle pasture with abundant dung beetles is largely free of surface dung during the warmer months of the year, when the dung beetles are most active. The soil in such a pasture will be deep and rich compared to a pasture with few or no dung beetles. In contrast, where dung beetles have been eliminated, dung accumulates on the surface until it is washed away in heavy rains. The soil in such a pasture gradually degrades, as nutrients are removed but not replaced. Without dung beetles, the ground is also likely to become hard-packed, so any rain that falls is more likely to run off than to soak in. For all those reasons, dung beetles are among the most important groups of animals for maintaining pasture fertility and productivity.

The males do the dung-rolling in most species, but there is usually a female in attendance, who will lay eggs in the dung once it is buried. In many species, you may see one beetle riding on the ball of dung as a passenger as another beetle pushes the ball along. The dung beetle on the ball is the female, and the one doing the pushing is the male. In some species, the female may assist the male in pushing the ball, and in still others, the female follows along behind as the male pushes the ball. In any case, if you look closely, you will see two beetles moving along with each ball of dung.

At least one African species of dung beetle is known to use polarized light from moonlight to navigate at night. On moonless nights, they can even use the Milky Way to navigate. Our Texas rollers, however, seem to be most active by day.

You may be most familiar with the beetles as they push balls of dung along on the ground, but if you watch a fresh pile of dung, you will see the beetles as they fly into the prize. They can smell fresh dung and fly in as soon as it is on the ground. In a pasture with healthy populations of dung beetles, there is intense competition for the dung.

As important as dung beetles are for the health of rangelands, you would think that ranchers would be careful to maintain healthy populations of these insects. Many ranchers do understand the beetles' importance and are careful with their use of insecticides. Unfortunately, some popular insecticides used for deworming cattle (such as ivermectin) are highly toxic to dung beetles. Although the ivermectin is applied directly to cattle, the cattle absorb it and then excrete it in their dung. The ivermectin in the dung poisons the dung beetles and their larvae and can eliminate them from a pasture. Over time, a pasture without dung beetles loses fertility and becomes hard-packed, and eventually it is far less productive for grasses.

One day, a visitor to the Double Helix Ranch came to pick up a couple of heifers he had purchased. He didn't warn me that he was coming, so we had to ride around and find my herd. As we did, we had the following conversation:

"Wow, you have great grass in this pasture! How long has it been since your cattle were in here?" the visitor asked.

"They have been in here since last fall," I responded.

"No way! There is so much grass, and I have not seen a single cow pie!"

"The cattle dung doesn't stay on the surface for long," I said, "especially this time of year. It gets buried quickly by dung beetles. All that buried dung improves and fertilizes my soil, so the grass grows well here."

"I've seen dung beetles at my ranch, too, but they don't begin to get rid of all my dung."

At this point, I spotted my herd. "There they are, let me show you my dung beetles."

I pointed out a fresh dung pile, quickly disappearing as dung beetles carried it away. "That's amazing!" he exclaimed. "Where did you get all these dung beetles?"

"I just don't poison them, and they multiply quickly. We have quite a diversity of different species."

He looked a little defensive as he responded. "I don't poison my dung beetles, either, but I sure don't have them like this."

"Do you deworm your cattle?" I asked.

"Yes, ivermectin, twice a year."

"The ivermectin ends up in the cattle dung, and it is highly toxic to dung beetles. Even when it doesn't kill the adults directly, it kills their larvae as they consume the provisioned dung balls."

He thought about that as he watched the masses of dung beetles remove the pile of fresh dung. "Well, how do you deworm your cattle? They look great, so why don't they have worms?"

I answered, "Well, with no dung on the surface, there is no place for the cattle parasites to breed. So, they don't infect the cattle to begin with. If I ever develop problems, there are some dung-beetle-safe alternatives."

All that money and effort that people spend on insecticides and dewormers is largely counterproductive. They aren't just poisoning the species that they target. The agrochemical companies make huge profits by convincing people to "kill, baby, kill." The more you use the insecticides, the more you will need to use them. It is a very profitable scheme, for the companies. For the producer (especially on a family ranch or farm), it just degrades the land and cuts into profits. Biodiversity is good for the land, good for profits, and good for health and sustainability.

There are alternative deworming drugs that are thought to be relatively dung-beetle safe, and they are usually marketed with this noted benefit. In a pasture with good populations of dung beetles, however, dung is quickly cleaned up, and cattle are much less likely to become heavily infected with parasites in the first place. Ironically, when deworming also kills dung beetles, then dung accumulates, which benefits cattle parasites. Then even more deworming becomes necessary. By maintaining a pasture with healthy dung beetle populations, ranchers can break this vicious cycle, and they often find that they can eliminate or greatly reduce expensive deworming treatments.

The next time you see a pair of dung beetles rolling a ball of dung along, you might stop to marvel at their efforts and give them a little thanks for their important service.

20

Where Have All the Quail Gone?

ʌ A Bobwhite covey visiting a water hole for a drink. *Photo by Melody Lytle.*

Anyone who is over 60 and grew up in rural Texas knows that wildlife in the state today is very different from the wild-life of their childhood. They may remember quail hunting, when many coveys of quail could be seen every day. Or they may remember horny toads (Texas Horned Lizards), which every Texas child of the 1960s and 1970s remembers with fondness but almost no one under 50 remembers at all. Or they may remember that Ornate Box Turtles were once common across the Hill Country, but they probably haven't seen one in the last 20 years. Why have all these species declined?

All those declines are connected to a set of common reasons that have resulted in major changes in the wildlife of the Hill Country. Like most things, the answers are not simple. Multiple reasons combine to produce the overall problem. But there are things we can do to reverse the declines.

The reasons for the declines include loss or degradation of habitat (of species that include the insect prey base, such as native Harvester Ants), introduction and increase of exotic species, and increases of some medium-sized predators such as raccoons. Let's consider why each of these problems exists.

The loss of an appropriate food base is partly a function of the indiscriminate use of pesticides by humans. Imported South American Fire Ants became a problem across most of the Hill Country in the 1980s and 1990s. Unfortunately, many people have trouble telling a fire ant from any other ant, and the most obvious ants we have in the Hill Country are the native and beneficial Harvester Ants. Harvester Ants help native grasses spread and germinate, they aerate the soil, and they are the principal food source for Texas Horned Lizards. But widespread poisoning programs directed at imported fire ants strongly affected Harvester Ants as well, leading to the unfortunate decline of these beneficial insects. With fewer Harvester Ants to eat, Texas Horned Lizards declined.

The Texas Horned Lizard (and our local quail, the Northern Bobwhite, among many other species) faced other problems in the late 1900s as well. The rapid increase of exotic fire ants and feral hogs led to the consumption and reduction of many ground-nesting species. Both imported fire ants and feral hogs eat the eggs or hatchlings of quail, lizards, and other species that lay their eggs on or in the ground.

At the same time, native medium-sized predators (termed meso-predators) such as raccoons exploded across the Hill Country (as did the feral hog populations). The increase in hogs and raccoons is largely the result of increased supplemental feeding of wildlife, targeted at deer and birds. Unfortunately, if no efforts are made to exclude hogs and raccoons, much of this wildlife feed goes to those nontarget species.

Traditionally, raccoon and hog populations were controlled either by larger predators (such as Coyotes) or by human trapping and hunting. But trapping of raccoons greatly declined when the raccoon pelt market crashed in the early 1980s. I've talked with many people who grew up in the Hill Country in the 1960s and 1970s who trapped raccoons and sold their pelts for spending money. That is no longer practical today, because the pelts are nearly worthless. In addition, the nonhuman predators of raccoons (largely Coyotes and Bobcats) have bounties on them in many counties of central Texas. With fewer human and other predators, and an increased food supply from year-round supplemental feeding of wildlife, it is no wonder that raccoon populations have exploded. Raccoons love to eat almost any small vertebrate they can catch, and they love the eggs of almost everything (whether quail, lizards, or turtles).

What can we do to reverse these declines? Fortunately, imported fire ants are not as much of a problem as they were around the turn of the millennium. Researchers from the University of Texas have introduced a tiny fly (called a phorid) that specializes in parasitizing imported fire ants, and those introductions have helped to reduce the density and activity of these ants. With the decline in fire ants, people are using fewer products designed to kill ants, the fire ants are less active by day, and beneficial Harvester Ants are slowly beginning to recover.

The boom in hogs and mesopredator populations requires more work, but it is a problem that can be addressed. Although trapping and controlling hogs and raccoons is a lot of effort, it is important to return our natural ecosystems to balance. Rather than putting bounties on Coyotes and Bobcats, we should consider offering incentives to control feral hogs and raccoon populations. Coyotes and other large predators are important to control hogs, raccoons, and even deer populations. Our White-tailed Deer populations in most of the Hill Country are far above optimal, which results in poor nourishment and unhealthy deer. Some people may enjoy calling and hunting Coyotes and Bobcats, but this practice is not beneficial to maintaining balance and diversity among our other native species. Our wildlife populations would be much better off if our management efforts focused instead on the problematic feral hog and raccoon populations. Such control would also prove highly beneficial to farmers and ranchers, as the booming hog and raccoon populations result in enormous agricultural losses each year.

If you miss the quail, horned lizards, frogs, turtles, and other wildlife that you remember from your youth, there is something that you can do about it. First, if you practice supplemental feeding of deer or birds, use methods that exclude nontarget species such as hogs and raccoons. Second, encourage the control of problematic species such as raccoons and hogs, rather than apex predators such as Coyotes, Bobcats, or Mountain Lions (which prey on hogs and raccoons). Third, be careful and restrictive with the use of broad-spectrum insecticides. Fourth, support habitat restoration projects and the return of native vegetation. Those simple steps can mean the difference between healthy, diverse wildlife populations and boring landscapes with nothing left but introduced species.

21

Grasshoppers, Locusts, and Plagues

ʌ Differential Grasshoppers. These relatives of the extinct Rocky Mountain Locust sometimes plague the Hill Country today.

I n 1875, an enormous plague of locusts moved across the Great Plains of North America, from Canada to Texas, eating everything in its path. (Locusts are a special form of swarming, migratory grasshoppers that are stimulated to change their color and behavior when conditions become crowded.) The species that formed the 1875 swarm was the Rocky Mountain Locust, *Melanoplus spretus*. This grasshopper once bred in sandy soils across just a few thousand square miles of the northern Rocky Mountain states and southern Canada. In favorable years, crowding would initiate migratory behavior in the grasshoppers, and they would sweep down into the Great Plains in almost unbelievable numbers.

Throughout the 1700s and 1800s, periodic swarms of Rocky Mountain Locusts caused serious damage to agricultural crops and grazing land, consuming everything from leather to wood to wool. Trains were sometimes stopped by the huge accumulations of grasshoppers on the tracks. The 1875 swarm was estimated to cover about 198,000 square miles at any one time, as it moved across the continent devastating all plant life in its path. The weight of grasshoppers in the plague was estimated at 27.5 million tons, based on an estimate of 12.5 trillion (12,500,000,000,000) individuals in the swarm.

Then, suddenly, this species went extinct. The last living specimens of Rocky Mountain Locusts were seen in southern Canada in 1902. Ironically, because the species was so abundant, relatively few specimens were ever collected and preserved in insect collections. Why it went extinct is largely unknown, although the best guess is that agricultural plowing of the sandy soils where it laid its eggs resulted in its elimination.

Despite the disappearance of this troublesome species, outbreaks of other species of grasshoppers still cause considerable agricultural damage in many parts of the western United States and in many other regions of the world. Our local grasshopper outbreaks in the Hill Country can be impressive and annoying, but rarely is the damage anything like that endured by early settlers of the Hill Country in the 1800s.

We have many local species of grasshoppers, but the one that causes the greatest agricultural problems in the Hill Country these days is the Differential Grasshopper, *Melanoplus differentialis*. This grasshopper is in the same genus as the Rocky Mountain Locust. Unlike that now-extinct plague-causing species, the Differential Grasshopper is not migratory, and it has only one generation per year. Individuals move no more than a few miles from where they are born. Although these grasshoppers can occur in very large numbers locally, they do not form the migratory plagues of locusts that were witnessed by Hill Country residents in the late 1800s.

Each female Differential Grasshopper lays up to six egg masses in sandy soil, and each egg mass can contain up to 200 eggs. That means that a single female grasshopper can produce more than 1,000 offspring. This is why our grasshopper populations can vary so much from one year to the next. When weather conditions are favorable, huge numbers of grasshoppers emerge in the spring and develop through the summer on the Edwards Plateau.

The eggs of a Differential Grasshopper start development shortly after they are laid. They then enter a resting period, known as diapause, and remain in a holding pattern through the winter. When the soil warms in late spring, development resumes and the young grasshoppers (known as nymphs) hatch, usually in late May. The nymphs look like small, wingless versions of the adult grasshoppers; as they go through five life stages, or instars, each successive stage looks more like the mature adult. Only the final adult stage has wings. The growth of the nymphs takes about a month, and then the adults live and reproduce for another couple of months. That is why we have lots of grasshoppers through our summer but relatively few during the rest of the year.

Differential Grasshoppers eat both grasses and broad-leaved forbs, and they can be devastating to agricultural crops. Locally, they are especially problematic for home gardeners, as well as for those with vineyards or orchards. When the weather turns dry, the grasshoppers often focus their feeding on irrigated crops and trees. In some years, grasshoppers can strip all the leaves from fruit trees or vines, consume all the fruit, and even girdle tree limbs by consuming bark.

As frustrating as they can be, large populations of grasshoppers do have some benefits. In particular, grasshoppers are an important food of many birds, lizards, frogs, and other wildlife. Large grasshopper populations are associated with increased reproductive success of quail, turkeys, and many other birds. For this reason, landowners should carefully consider the measures they use to control grasshopper populations. Insecticides that poison grasshoppers also poison their predators, and the poisons rapidly accumulate in species that feed on grasshoppers, which can result in reproductive failure or even death of many species of birds. One of the most common questions I get from local landowners is, "What happened to all the quail?" There are several reasons for quail decline, but increased use of insecticides is certainly a contributing factor.

There are several alternatives to insecticides for the control or management of large grasshopper populations. For home gardeners, one of the simplest solutions is to use insect netting over and around plants that grasshoppers target in the summer. During the long, hot, dry days of summer, the light shading effect of the netting is also beneficial to most plants. The use of cayenne pepper sprays on plants can also discourage grasshopper feeding, as long as there are alternative food plants available to the grasshoppers.

When our grasshopper populations get high on the Double Helix Ranch, I collect them off my fruit trees and garden plants at night and freeze them by the gallon. Then I have a supply that I can feed to our chickens through the winter. There isn't much that chickens like better than grasshoppers.

Another popular solution is to use biological control to reduce grasshopper populations around sensitive crops and gardens. Tiny internal parasites of grasshoppers, known as microsporidia, can infect and kill the early instars of grasshoppers. One such species, *Nosema locustae*, is available commercially (commonly abbreviated as NoLo). The infectious NoLo are sold in a bait that is attractive to the grasshopper nymphs; as the nymphs eat the bait, they also ingest the microsporidia. Once in the grasshopper's gut, the microsporidia quickly replicate, and the grasshoppers stop feeding and die. Other grasshoppers eat the bodies of the affected grasshoppers, spreading the infection and greatly reducing grasshopper numbers.

Although the microsporidians are lethal to the early instars of grasshoppers, they are not very effective in controlling adult grasshoppers, and they are harmless to most other species, including grasshopper predators, pets, and humans. Applied properly, early in the grasshopper life cycle, NoLo is a highly effective way to reduce grasshopper populations locally around gardens and orchards without harming birds and other grasshopper predators.

Finally, I'll note that grasshoppers are considered a delicacy by humans in many parts of the world. I have eaten them in many parts of Asia, Africa, and Latin America, where they are relished as a healthy and tasty protein source. They may not appeal to everyone, but if you want to give them a try, a quick internet search will reveal many recipes. Some species of grasshoppers are far more edible than others, however, and be sure that any that you eat have not been feeding on crops that have been treated with insecticides.

22

The History of Texas Cattle Written in Their DNA

ʌ A Texas Longhorn bull, a modern descendant of 500 years of Texas cattle history. This is D-H Cinco de Mayo, the herd sire on the Double Helix Ranch.

When German settlers arrived in the Hill Country in the 1850s, they found bountiful oak–grassland savannas occupied by herds of wild, long-horned cattle. After the Civil War ended in 1865, the wild cattle became a key to the settlers' survival, as they were rounded up and herded to railheads in Kansas to feed a hungry nation that had been ravaged by war. Fred Gibson's novel *Old Yeller* is set in this post–Civil War period in the Texas Hill Country, as the young character Travis experiences adventures with his dog while his father is away on one such cattle drive.

Where did these wild cattle come from? I persuaded one of my graduate students, Emily Jane McTavish, to address this question in detail by comparing the genomes of Texas Longhorns and other modern cattle. Her dissertation uncovered and confirmed a complex history of repeated domestication, rewilding, and redomestication.

About 10,000 years ago, humans living in two different parts of Eurasia began keeping and raising "Wild Beasts," or aurochs. One area of domestication was in the Middle East, and the other was on the Indian subcontinent. From the Middle East, cattle domestication spread across Europe. The more tropically adapted cattle of India spread throughout much of southern Asia and westward into Africa. For thousands of years, these two strains of domesticated cattle were developed independently for meat and dairy production.

When the Moors invaded the Iberian Peninsula of Europe from northern Africa in the eighth century, they brought their cattle from Africa, which then mixed with the cattle of Hispania. They also moved cattle back to Africa, thus mixing cattle from the two original domestication events. This mixing produced large, hardy cattle that were excellent beef animals and that also had genes that allowed them to thrive in hot, dry landscapes. In the 1400s, Spanish and Portuguese colonists took some of these mixed-breed cattle to the Canary Islands, where they thrived.

In 1493, Christopher Columbus set sail from Spain on his second voyage to the New World, with 17 ships and 1,200 men, intending to establish permanent colonies. On the way, he stopped in the Canary Islands, where he picked up pregnant heifers to establish cattle at the new Spanish settlements in Hispaniola.

Cattle thrived in Hispaniola, and by the early 1500s, the Spanish took descendants of these cattle to Veracruz, on the Gulf Coast of Mexico. As the Spanish explored Mexico, they took cattle with them for food, but many of the cattle escaped or were released in the wild, where they multiplied. Soon, herds of feral cattle were roaming across northern Mexico, into what would become Texas.

These feral herds of cattle faced many predators, including

Mountain Lions, Wolves, and Grizzly Bears. Cows that could defend their calves were more likely to leave descendants, so there was strong natural selection for longer horns, which the cows used to "hook" would-be predators. As had been true in the days of wild aurochs, bulls had to fight for dominance of their herd, and the largest, longest-horned bulls also had the advantage in these fights. Thus, from generation to generation, the cattle with the longest horns survived and left the most offspring, just as had once been true among wild aurochs. By the time German settlers arrived in Texas in the 1850s, the distinctive long-horned feral cattle would come to be known as Texas Longhorns.

Initially, the Longhorns were rounded up and sold for meat and tallow. Then, as barbed wire came to Texas in the 1870s, it became feasible to fence and raise cattle, and the Longhorns were returned to domestication. In the late 1800s and early 1900s cattle were valued especially for their tallow (which was used to make candles, the primary means for light at night). Soon fatter European breeds were brought in, and pure herds of Texas Longhorns had nearly disappeared by the early 1900s. J. Frank Dobie and others worked to preserve the last of the breed in the 1920s, and today's Longhorns are the result of those efforts.

Today, about 10–15 percent of the genes of a Texas Longhorn are descended from the Indian domestication event, with the rest coming from the Middle Eastern domestication event. The period of wild natural selection that produced the long horns of Texas Longhorns also helped select for genes that make Texas Longhorns resistant to diseases, tolerant of heat and drought, and able to give easy, unassisted birth to their calves. Those genetic traits are of considerable interest to modern cattle breeders, who are now taking advantage of the complex history of the once-feral cattle of Texas to develop new, hardy breeds of cattle. These cattle breeds are better suited for grass-fed beef production on native range.

We raise Texas Longhorns on the Double Helix Ranch, and they live in social groups much as their wild ancestors did. The Longhorn cows are highly effective at protecting their calves, and we never experience any problems with predators attacking our cattle.

We still have healthy populations of Coyotes on the ranch, and the occasional Mountain Lion, but neither of these predators ever bother the Longhorns.

Our cattle are important for maintaining our grasslands, which were grazed by a mix of Longhorns and American Bison until the late 1800s. Some grazing is important to disturb the soil, to plant grass seeds, and to break down grass into nutrients that replenish the soil. Dung beetles are an important component of this process as well, as they bury the cattle dung in the soil. Without any large grazers, grasslands are hard to maintain over time. On the other hand, too much grazing can kill perennial grasses. Without seasonal migration (as was once the case with bison), it is important to rotate grazers among pastures, to simulate a similar pattern of seasonal grazing and give grasses a chance to recover after they have been grazed.

Sunrise over a meadow of Hill Country wildflowers in June. ➤

V

IN THE WOODLANDS AND BRUSHLANDS

Parts of the Edwards Plateau are covered in dense woodlands, especially of juniper and oak. As a consequence, many plants and animals of the eastern North American woodlands extend their ranges westward onto the Edwards Plateau. In some cases, the isolation of these populations led to the evolution of new, related species that are now endemic to the Hill Country.

Other groups that are found throughout the wooded mountains of the Sierra Madre Oriental in Mexico extend north onto the Edwards Plateau. Still other species that are found mostly in the Rocky Mountains to the west range eastward into the Texas Hill

≺ Ferns and other understory plants in a wooded Hill Country canyon.

Country. The result is a fascinating combination of eastern, western, and tropical woodland species living side by side in the woodlands and canyons of the Edwards Plateau.

The wettest woodlands of the Hill Country are in deep, protected canyons, especially where rivers drain off the Plateau to the east and south. In these wet, rocky canyons, northern species like Canadian Columbine are found side by side with southeastern Palmettos, northeastern Bigtooth Maples (relatives of Sugar Maples), and subtropical Madrones. Eastern treefrogs, tropical direct-developing rainfrogs, and toads from the east, west, north, and south all live side by side as well, as do many diverse groups of insects, mammals, birds, and other animals.

Even outside the protected canyons, the extensive woodlands come as a surprise to many first-time visitors to the Hill Country. Giant Bald Cypress trees line the rivers; Pecans, Black Hickories, Black and Little Walnuts, Escarpment Cherries, Netleaf Hackberries, and Gum Bumelias grow in deeper soils; Ashe Junipers cover rocky slopes; and oak savannas are found across the Plateau. Here, most trees tend to branch and spread out closer to the ground than they do in eastern or northern forests, making the woodlands of the Texas Hill Country look more like those of the Sierra Madre of Mexico than the characteristic forests of much of the United States and Canada.

23

Containing and Preventing Oak Wilt

⋏ Plateau Live Oak, *Quercus fusiformis.*

P arts of the Hill Country are known for majestic oak trees, and most of the Edwards Plateau is best described as oak–juniper woodland and savanna. Although nine species of oaks—Plateau Live Oak, Post Oak, Blackjack Oak, Spanish Oak, White Shin Oak, Lacey Oak, Mexican White Oak, Bur Oak, and Chinquapin Oak—are native to the Hill Country, some combination of the first six of these oaks dominates in most areas. The Plateau Live Oak tends to be the primary oak found in rocky areas and along ridges, whereas the Post Oak and Blackjack Oak thrive where sandy, granitic soils accumulate. Spanish Oaks and White Shin Oaks are mostly confined to areas of limestone outcrops. Lacey Oaks are abundant in the canyonlands and southern escarpments of the Hill Country, whereas the much rarer Mexican White Oak is native along major rivers of the western Plateau (especially the Devils River). The relatively uncommon Bur Oak and Chinquapin Oak are usually found near springs or other water in deep valley soils and protected canyons.

Given the predominance of oaks in our landscapes, anything that threatens these trees is a concern. The extreme drought year of 2011 killed many centuries-old oak trees and caused dieback and stress to many of the survivors. The dead remains of giant oak trees will punctuate our woodlands for years to come.

With the loss and stress to our oak trees from drought, oak diseases have become an increasing concern. In particular, oak wilt is a worry for many Hill Country landowners, and I'm often asked what causes oak wilt and what we can do to prevent or control it. Oak wilt is an often fatal disease of oaks that has been especially devastating in parts of the Edwards Plateau and surrounding areas.

Oak wilt disease is caused by the oak wilt fungus, which has the scientific name *Bretziella fagacearum*. Although not native to the United States, the fungus was first detected in Wisconsin in 1944. Recent evidence suggests that it may have been introduced from Central or South America. Once introduced into North America, it quickly spread across the Midwest and then south into Texas.

There are three main groups of oak trees—the red oaks (sometimes called black oaks), the white oaks, and the live oaks (the last are actually a distinct subgroup of white oaks). Our red oaks include Blackjack Oak and Spanish Oak, whereas Plateau Live Oak is a live oak, and the rest of our oaks are species of white oaks. The red oaks are particularly susceptible to oak wilt fungus, although live oaks have little resistance as well. On the Edwards Plateau, large areas dominated by Plateau Live Oak have experienced massive die-offs, especially in the southern and eastern regions of the Plateau.

Oak wilt fungus is a parasite that invades the tree's vascular system. Once it infects a tree, it begins to choke off water and nutrients in infected branches. In red oaks, the effects are swift and fatal. The leaves of an infected tree begin to wilt and turn bronze within a few weeks of infection (usually starting at the ends of branches), and the tree then drops its leaves and dies within a few months. The fungus then forms a tan or grayish mat of growth under the bark of the tree that smells like fermenting fruit. This mat often results in the splitting or slipping of the bark of the tree.

The progression of disease in live oaks is somewhat slower, although the end result is largely the same. The leaf bronzing usually starts along the veins of the leaves, with areas away from the veins retaining green coloration. Branches may die off one at a time, over the course of a few years, followed by the death of the tree. The fungal mats that form under the bark of red oaks rarely form on live oaks or white oaks.

Oak wilt is spread in several ways. The fermenting smell of the fungal mats that form under the bark of infected red oaks is attractive to a group of sap-feeding beetles called nitidulids. The beetles carry the spores of the fungus to wounds on uninfected trees, where the spores infect the wounded tree. The spores are produced during periods of cool, wet weather, as in the spring when the trees are rapidly growing. To reduce the possibility of oak wilt spread, it is especially important not to trim or injure oak trees in the spring growing season. Any time of year, any cuts or wounds on oak trees should be immediately treated with wound paints, which will reduce the possibility of infection by fungal spores.

Another common way for oak wilt to spread is through the transport of infected firewood. Dead oak trees are often sources for firewood, and infected wood will contain the spores of the oak wilt fungus. Therefore, never move or use wood from areas of oak wilt infection. If you cut down an infected red oak, cover the woodpile with clear plastic, cover the edges of the plastic with soil, and leave it for at least a summer. The plastic will act like a greenhouse, and the fungus will be killed by the high temperatures.

Once oak wilt infections occur, they can be very difficult to treat or contain. The roots of oak trees often merge or graft with one another, and the fungus can move from one tree to another through such roots. At this point, the primary way to slow movement of the fungus among adjacent trees is physical trenching between the trees, to prevent the roots from intermingling. The trenches, however, need to be at least four feet deep to be effective.

For the most valuable trees, injection of fungicides can sometimes prevent or slow infections. Such treatments are expensive and labor-intensive, requiring the services of a professional arborist. Although progress has been made in treatments of oak wilt, they are usually not practical across large areas of infection involving many trees.

Finally, if you plan to plant an oak tree in your yard or property, consider selecting one of the more resistant white oak species, rather than a red oak or live oak. Then, even if oak wilt comes to your neighborhood or ranch, your oak tree will be more likely to survive.

24

The Challenges of Being an Oak Tree in the Hill Country

⋀ December in the Hill Country. The Spanish Oaks are turning red, while the Plateau Live Oaks and Ashe Junipers remain green through the winter.

When we think of the many features that make the Hill Country of central Texas so attractive (to humans, as well as to our diverse native flora and fauna), our beautiful oak savannas come immediately to mind. Most of our oaks are distinctively different in growth form and character from the dense, closed-canopy oak forests found in the eastern United States. Eastern oaks must compete with one another, and with many other forest trees, for access to sunlight, so they grow tall and straight toward the canopy, reaching for a little piece of sky.

In contrast, our Hill Country oaks have access to abundant sunlight. They branch out relatively close to the ground and spread their branches far and wide. Our most abundant oak species, the Plateau Live Oak, keeps green leaves all year long, dropping its leaves in the spring as it grows a new set. Live oaks may not grow especially tall (at least in comparison to many eastern oak trees), but they make up in breadth what they lack in height. Many visitors to the Hill Country marvel at our ancient, twisted, sprawling oaks with branches so low that they sometimes touch the ground. Children (and adults who retain the heart of a child) take delight in climbing high into these magnificent and ancient branching labyrinths.

If our oaks are not limited by sunlight, then why aren't there more of them? Why are our oak woodlands relatively open, with scattered trees separated by grasslands and fields of wildflowers? And why are most of the oak trees one encounters many centuries old? Where are all the young oak trees?

Perhaps the biggest limitation our oaks face is access to water. Plants use energy from sunlight to convert water and carbon dioxide into oxygen and carbohydrates. To get access to the carbon dioxide in the atmosphere, they need to open tiny portals in their leaves, called stomata. When the stomata open, carbon dioxide can enter the leaf, but at the same time, water vapor exits the leaf (a process called transpiration). A giant oak tree needs to draw enormous quantities of water from its roots to its leaves so that it can grow through photosynthesis.

Our drought-prone climate and thin rocky soils make it difficult for oaks to pull enough water to the leaves, especially in the heat of the summer. Tall, straight oaks could not survive here, as they need to pull water much higher from the ground.

Live oaks are our most common oak largely because they are our most drought-tolerant species. If you compare a live-oak leaf with the leaf from most other oak species, you will immediately notice that it is thicker, stiffer, and smaller. Those characteristics are adaptations that help the tree survive in a dry environment. Live oaks can close their stomata and lose relatively little water to the atmosphere, compared with many other oak species.

When you walk around much of the Hill Country, notice that about the only oaks found on rocky ridges are live oaks. If you live in a part of the Hill Country with limestone outcrops (rather than granite or gneiss), the ridges may support Shin Oaks or Lacey Oaks as well. In either case, you'll likely notice that few of these oaks appear to be ancient, in contrast to the oaks in the valleys. In the past decade, many of the oaks on these ridges have died back—mostly the result of the devastating 2011 drought. In many places, they are sprouting back from the roots, but the tops of the trees did not survive the drought. The small trees on rocky ridges are likely much older than they appear; their top growth has just died and grown back through a series of droughts. Although the 2011 drought was a record drought from a human perspective, tree rings suggest that central Texas has endured similar droughts once every century or so. With global climate change, such droughts are expected to become more frequent.

Soil washes from ridgetops into valleys, where it accumulates. In areas with deeper soils and better access to groundwater, live oaks can survive for many centuries and through many severe droughts. That is why you will find the largest, oldest, most picturesque trees in valleys and other areas of deep soil. This is also where you find most of our other oak species, including Post Oak, Texas Red Oak, and Blackjack Oak. A few of our oaks are even more dependent on deep soils and reliable access to water, so look for Bur Oaks and Chinquapin Oaks near water sources.

In wet years, our oaks produce abundant crops of acorns, which are of course the seeds of oak trees, enclosed in a leathery shell. These acorns will germinate only if they are buried before they dry out. Acorns are rich in proteins, carbohydrates, and fats that are used to nourish the oak seedling, so they are also sought out as a preferred food by many animals, including deer, feral pigs, squirrels, turkeys, and even some humans. All this competition for acorns means that very few acorns successfully sprout into oak seedlings, and even then many of the oak seedlings are consumed by deer and other browsers.

The huge crops of acorns in wet years are actually a means of achieving reproductive success on the part of the oaks. Just as you are likely to put up extra food in your refrigerator and forget about it, squirrels and other small mammals bury many extra acorns so that they will have a cache of food for the winter. Some of these acorns are never retrieved, and they are the ones that germinate into the next generation of oaks.

The reason that many oaks in a given area appear to be of a similar age is that the conditions for oak recruitment are somewhat specialized. Our oaks need a series of wet years to become established, and the densities of deer and other browsers can't be so high that all of the seedling oaks are consumed. Right now, our deer and feral pig populations are too high for much successful oak recruitment, which is why you are likely to see many more ancient oak trees than young ones.

As you enjoy the shade of an ancient oak this summer, marvel over the fact that it has beaten extremely long odds to exist, and that it may have been here since long before the first European colonists arrived on our shores. Through all those centuries, the oak's leaves, acorns, and branches have provided critical resources to countless native plants, lichens, and animals.

25

How Do Trees Sense When It Is Time to Leaf Out and Bloom?

⋏ A Mexican Plum bursting into bloom on the Double Helix Ranch.

After a late cold snap in the spring, have you worried that your plants might not recover from freeze damage, or wondered how trees sense that the time is right to leaf out and bloom?

Native trees and plants rarely experience any trouble with Hill Country winter freezes, because they are adapted to our local climate. Even though winter lows in the single digits (Fahrenheit) are not typical of most of our winters, such low temperatures occur every decade or so. Plants that can't survive those lows simply don't exist here for long periods of time. Our native trees and other plants will have no trouble surviving such a cold snap by staying dormant, or by producing appropriate antifreeze compounds. Their adaptation to our local environment includes tolerance for extremes that may occur only a few times a century.

The problems that people experience with freezing plants usually involve nonnative ornamentals, garden vegetables, and fruit trees. Many fruit trees, including apples, apricots, peaches, pears, plums, and persimmons, are quite cold tolerant and should be fine in freezes as long as they are appropriate varieties for our area. Peach tree varieties require anywhere from 100 to more than 1,000 chilling hours—the number of hours each winter that fall between freezing and 45°F (7°C). The Hill Country typically ranges from about 600 to 900 chilling hours a year, and there are many peach varieties with chilling requirements that fall in that range. As long as you plant one of the appropriate varieties, you should have relatively little to worry about. When the appropriate number of chilling hours have passed, then warm weather will stimulate dormant buds to start growing—after the average date for our last freeze of the spring. A late spring freeze may still kill the blooms in an extreme year, but most years the tree will fruit normally.

If you plant a variety of fruit tree with low chilling hours, however, it will leaf out and bloom well before our average last freeze, which means the tree will likely be killed in late winter or spring freezes, or the blooms will be damaged so that no fruit sets. If you plant a fruit tree variety that requires a high number of chilling hours (above 900 hours, for example), then it will probably leaf out late and likely never bloom or set fruit in most years. Therefore, it is important to select fruit tree varieties that are close in their chill-hour requirements to local average annual chill hours.

Perhaps you are wondering at this point, "How do the trees count chill hours?" In other words, how do the trees sense how many chill hours have passed? In the fall, when trees begin to experience low temperatures, they produce a hormone that causes the tree to go into dormancy. As long as this hormone remains in the tree, the tree will remain dormant. For most fruit trees, the hormone breaks down in cool temperatures, within a range of about 32° to 45°F (0° to 7°C). Different fruit tree varieties produce differing amounts of the dormancy hormone, so they require different numbers of chilling hours to break down enough of the hormone to end dormancy. After the dormancy hormone has broken down, then warm weather will stimulate new growth. If sufficient chilling hours haven't passed to break down the dormancy hormone, then a warm spell in the middle of winter will not result in premature bud growth.

Many flowering plants use another mechanism to determine when it is appropriate to bloom. They contain one or more light-sensitive proteins that can sense the change in day length (the photoperiod) as the season progresses. The critical factor is actually the length of the night, when the protein is not detecting light. The nights get shorter as we move from winter to spring to summer, and many plants use the changing length of the night to sense the appropriate season for blooming. For many plants, blooming is timed to match the arrival or emergence of appropriate pollinators for their flowers. For example, you may have noticed that many of our native red-flowered plants start blooming right about the time that our Black-chinned Hummingbirds return from tropical parts of Mexico and Central America. Both the flowers and the hummingbirds are using photoperiod clues to match the appropriate dates for blooming and arrival.

Introduced plants that are not native to our area may become established if they come from an area that has a similar climate, photoperiod, and soil type. Several trees that were originally planted as ornamentals (such as Chinaberry, Tree-of-Heaven, and Chinese Tallow) have since escaped and become invasive (growing and reproducing on their own) in the Hill Country. Many grasses (such as King Ranch Bluestem and Johnsongrass) and forbs (such as Maltese Star Thistle and Annual Bastard Cabbage) have been introduced from other parts of the world and become invasive locally as well. Invasive plants can displace natives and become problematic, especially if they are not held in check by appropriate local herbivores and pathogens. It is therefore important to avoid planting species that might escape and become invasive locally. The best policy is to stick with native ornamentals and well-studied fruit and vegetable plants that are known not to escape human cultivation.

Many subtropical plants can grow in the Hill Country through our warmer winters, only to be killed back when we have an extreme cold spell. For example, I enjoy growing and eating pomegranates, but most pomegranate trees are easily killed back to the ground if the temperatures drop into the lower teens or single digits (as measured in Fahrenheit). When that happens, it requires several years for the tree to grow back large enough to start fruiting again, if it survives at all. I've developed a few practices to keep the pomegranates around my house from freezing back to the ground in extreme cold spells. First, I select pomegranate varieties from cold regions of the world, such as Turkmenistan or Uzbekistan, which are more cold-tolerant than the commercial varieties that are grown in California. Second, when extreme cold temperatures are in the forecast, I cover as much of the tree trunks as I can with old hay or other mulch. I then remove the mulch when the freezing conditions have passed. Although this permits subtropical trees to survive Hill Country winters, it obviously requires a lot of human effort. That is why subtropical trees like pomegranates are not expected to escape cultivation and become invasive in our area.

Rest assured that your native plants are more likely to survive our most extreme cold spells, as will planted fruit trees, as long as you have selected varieties that are appropriate for the Hill Country.

26

The Dr. Jekyll and Mr. Hyde
of Trees

⋏ A Honey Mesquite, the tree as tough as Texas.

I t is the best of trees; it is the worst of trees. Texans have long had a love-hate relationship with Honey Mesquite. In the right form, in the right place, mesquites can be among the most beautiful and useful of trees. They can also be some of the most annoying and troublesome woody vegetation on ranches in many parts of Texas.

Honey Mesquite has a deep taproot that may extend 100 feet or more below the surface, down to the water table. It also has an extensive lateral root system that gathers water from a wide area near the surface. Those features make mesquites among the most drought-resistant of trees in the Hill Country. In an extreme drought, they may drop their leaves to conserve water, but mesquites can survive droughts that kill almost any of our other trees.

Mesquites can live at least a couple of centuries. An old, single-trunked mesquite is a beautiful, majestic tree. The trunk and branches twist and turn to give it its characteristic shape. Its leaves sprout relatively late in the spring, so the soft green foliage is rarely caught by a late frost. The fragrant flowers of mesquite attract numerous pollinators, and its abundant nectar is a source of outstanding honey produced by bees, which gives Honey Mesquite its name.

Among the most important services that mesquites provide to the landscape is nitrogen fixation. Mesquite is a legume, and like other legumes, its roots produce nodules that host and support nitrogen-fixing rhizobia bacteria. All living organisms need nitrogen to make proteins, but most of the Earth's nitrogen is tied up in atmospheric nitrogen gas, which cannot be used directly by most of life. Rhizobia bacteria, however, can convert nitrogen gas into ammonia, which can be used by plants to make proteins. Animals then eat these plant proteins and thereby get the compounds that they need to make their own proteins. Thus, all of life depends on the action of these soil bacteria.

Legumes like mesquites (together with their bacterial symbionts) can add considerable amounts of fixed nitrogen to the ecosystem every year. This is a natural fertilization system that keeps the soil fertile and productive. If all the legumes are removed, soil fertility may plummet, and then farmers or ranchers need to add expensive nitrogen fertilizer to make up the difference.

The wood from mature mesquites is exquisite, with a deep, rich red core and yellowish outer layer. The wood is very dense and the grain is tight, so it takes on a beautiful fine polish. Mesquite wood is prized for making everything from fine tabletops to flooring, furniture, beautiful wooden bowls, and sculptures. Mesquite also makes some of the finest, longest-lasting firewood, and many people consider it among the very best woods for smoking barbecue.

In the frontier days, mesquite beans often provided the only available food in times of drought. They can be ground to make a sweet, nourishing flour, and they can also be used to make a substitute for coffee. Today, some diabetics seek out mesquite flour, because its sweetness comes from fructose rather than sucrose, and fructose can be digested without insulin. It also contains soluble fibers that help slow digestion and flatten a blood-sugar curve after eating.

There are few browsing animals alive in Texas today that will eat the leaves of a mesquite tree, except as a last resort. But when humans cut down a mesquite tree mechanically, the tree responds as if it had been browsed. By resprouting with many thorny branches from the cut stumps, the tree deters further browsing. This mesquite regrowth can become an impenetrable, thorny mess for a rancher.

If no browsers alive today are eating the mesquite, then why does it produce such thorny growth as a defense? What, exactly, is it defending its leaves against? The answer is that until a few thousand years ago, mesquite was browsed by mammoths and other large animals of the now-extinct Pleistocene megafauna. Although those large animals are long gone (due at least in part to the arrival of hunting humans in North America), mesquite still produces lots of thorns on its regrowth when it detects that it is being browsed. In essence, it is protecting itself from herbivory by large browsing animals that are now gone from the landscape.

Although the leaves of mesquite often go uneaten today, the sweetness in mesquite bean pods attracts many mammals. Uncrushed seeds pass through mammalian digestive systems intact, and the mammals then deposit the seeds in their feces. The stomach acids help the seeds to germinate; indeed, mesquite seeds need to pass through a digestive system in this way to sprout. Unfortunately, this means that mesquites can become highly invasive in certain situations—especially in overgrazed cattle pastures.

Because mesquites easily sprout from stumps, dense patches of invasive mesquite can be hard to control or remove. The mesquites either need to be grubbed out (cut well below the surface) or a tree-specific herbicide like Remedy needs to be applied directly to the stump as soon as it is cut. I generally avoid the use of herbicides, but this herbicide can be applied topically and carefully to avoid environmental contamination of surrounding areas. When thinning mesquite, it is good to remember that mesquite serves a very useful function in nitrogen fixation, so it is best to leave some of the larger, single-truck trees intact. This will remove the dense, thorny vegetation but leave some beautiful mature mesquites in a more natural configuration.

27

Spring Is Here, and So Are the Snakes

↑ A Broad-banded Copperhead in oak leaf litter.

As the weather warms, trees leaf out, and wildflowers burst forth on the landscape, many of us are eager to go out and enjoy the spring weather. Snakes become active in the spring as well, and that upsets many people. Here I will do my best to suggest that you relax a bit about snakes, and learn to watch and enjoy them. Once you learn to recognize the common species, you may find them beautiful, graceful, and fascinating to watch.

Why do so many people have such an aversion to snakes? We are trained from childhood to fear them, and the reasons are obvious—there are a few snakes that defend themselves (and obtain their food) through the use of venom. So, rather than learning to recognize and give wide berth to the few dangerous species, many parents train their children to fear and avoid all snakes. Unfortunately, that means that most people miss out on enjoying an important part of the Hill Country's native fauna.

Snakes play an important role in a functioning ecosystem, and their elimination causes many problems. Most larger snakes are efficient consumers of rodents. Rodents cause far more problems for people than do snakes—rodents carry serious diseases that can infect humans, and they do massive damage to our homes and agricultural crops. Elimination of snakes and other rodent predators can result in population booms of rodents. That's why many farmers are happy to have healthy populations of snakes around.

There are nearly 50 species of snakes in the Hill Country, and the few venomous species are easily recognized. Only two venomous snake species are common across most of the Hill Country—the Western Diamond-backed Rattlesnake and the Broad-banded Copperhead. Learn to recognize these two species on sight. They will not chase you; they want to get away from you more than you want to get away from them. I encounter and photograph them on a regular basis, and despite all my close encounters, I have never been bitten.

Rattlesnakes are a beautiful and iconic part of Texas, and once you realize that they will leave you alone if you leave them alone, you can marvel at the remarkable rattles that they use to warn of their presence. A rattlesnake would rather warn you of its presence with the noise from its rattle than waste some of its venom with a defensive bite. People come from all over the world to see the rattlesnakes of Texas. Besides the common Western Diamond-backed Rattlesnake, a few additional species live in the Hill Country, especially in western portions of the Edwards Plateau. All are easily recognized by their tail rattles. If you spot a rattlesnake, try watching it for a while, and let it go on its way. Rattlesnake populations have declined dramatically in recent decades, and it would be terrible if they went extinct. Imagine having to tell your grandchildren what a rattlesnake once was—that would be a sad day for Texas.

In the heat of the summer, most of my walks around our ranch are at night. With the cover of darkness and no one else around, I sometimes strip down to just my boots and enjoy the relative cool of the night air on my bare skin. On these late-night summer walks, I commonly observe Broad-banded Copperheads, and I'm always delighted to see them. They are one of our most attractive snakes, with alternating bands of dark and light orange, a pattern that blends in with fallen oak leaves, as the two sides of dead oak leaves have much the same coloration. That makes sense, as copperheads tend to favor oak mottes as habitat. Their heads are indeed distinctively copper-colored as well. They are unmistakable to anyone who has made the slightest effort to learn what a copperhead actually looks like. Despite this, I am constantly presented with all manner of photos of harmless snakes that have been killed because someone thought they were copperheads.

Copperhead bites are not common, as copperheads tend to mind their own business. The bite of a copperhead can be painful, but bites are rarely seriously dangerous to an adult human, as they are much smaller and the venom is not nearly as toxic as that of a rattlesnake.

Two other venomous snakes of the Texas Hill Country are not common, and are less frequently observed. Texas Coralsnakes occur across much of the Edwards Plateau, but they are rarely encountered, as they spend most of their time in leaf litter and beneath cover objects. They are easily recognized by their bright rings of red, yellow, and black, with the rings of the two warning colors (yellow and red) touching one another. (In our harmless milksnakes, the yellow and red rings are separated by black coloration.) A few Western Cottonmouths also live along some of the major Hill Country rivers. Almost any snake that lives in or around water is commonly mistaken for a cottonmouth, but the vast majority of these are harmless watersnakes of two species: the Blotched Watersnake and the Diamond-backed Watersnake. The former is common throughout waterways of almost any size across the Hill Country, whereas the latter is found around larger rivers and permanent ponds. Neither of these nonvenomous watersnakes poses any threat to humans.

How can you avoid being bitten by a snake? The simple answer is, leave it alone. The majority of snakebites in the United States occur when people attempt to kill or handle a snake. A few people are bitten each year when they step on, or accidentally grab, a venomous snake, so the other important advice is to watch where you put your hands and feet, especially if you are lifting or moving cover objects such as boards, rocks, or sheet metal. Wearing boots or snake chaps will protect against lower leg bites, and even long pants greatly reduce the chances of envenomation. When you spot a snake, just back off and give it some room, and then you can safely watch it and marvel at it.

If you learn to stop fearing snakes, and instead respect and enjoy them as a part of the natural history of Texas, you may find great new pleasure in the beauty, behavior, and diversity of snakes. Even if you still would rather not be around them, remember that they play an important part in the functioning of a healthy natural ecosystem, and leave them in peace.

28

Songs of the Summer Dog Days

⋏ A freshly emergent Dog-Day Cicada.

The ancient Greeks noticed that when the Dog Star Sirius, in the constellation Canis Major, was in the same part of the sky as the Sun, they could expect to experience the hottest days of the year. In this alignment, Sirius (which is the brightest star in the night sky) can be seen briefly just before dawn as a morning star. The Greeks associated the appearance of Sirius as a morning star with heat, drought, and the withering of crops (and also with the seasonal withering of men and arousal of women, but that is another story). To this day, we refer to the hottest days of summer, when Sirius is near the Sun in July and August (from our perspective here on Earth), as the dog days of summer.

We now understand that the heat of the summer is related to the tilt of the Earth and the angle of the sunlight that strikes the Earth as it revolves around the Sun, so the location of Sirius in the sky is nothing more than coincidental to summer. These days, most people pay a lot less attention to the location of stars in the night sky than they once did, so Texans likely associate summer with many things other than Sirius as an early morning star. Besides the obvious heat, you may associate summer with things like swimming, watermelons, peaches, hordes of ravenous grasshoppers, and the sounds of Dog-Day Cicadas as they chorus in our local oak trees.

Dog-Day Cicadas get their name because they emerge during the dog days of summer. We have several local species in the Hill Country, each of which has a distinct mating call, or song, and their songs are part of what makes the sound of summer nights distinctive. These calls are produced by the male cicadas, mostly by vibrating special structures called tymbals. Cicadas amplify the sound of these vibrating tymbals through body structures that act as resonance chambers, which helps explain why the calls can be so loud.

The species-specific male calls attract appropriate females as mates for the singers. After the cicadas mate, the females make small slits in the twigs of trees (usually on oaks, in the case of our local species) and deposit their eggs. The adults die soon thereafter (they live less than two months of their multiyear lives as adults). The eggs hatch into nymphs that drop to the ground and burrow beneath the surface. Once the nymphs are several feet underground, they feed on the sap (xylem) of tree roots. Nymphs develop through several juvenile stages underground and may stay there for many years before they emerge as adults and start the cycle over again.

When I start hearing large numbers of cicadas in the late summer, I also begin finding the emerging cicadas and their molted exoskeletons at the base of oak trees. The life cycles of our local cicadas are staggered, so similar numbers of individuals emerge every year. The emerging cicadas are eaten by various species of birds, mammals, and even some snakes (they are especially targeted by copperheads, which even climb into trees to find them).

You've likely either experienced firsthand or seen news reports of another kind of cicada, called Periodical Cicadas, that emerge in enormous numbers in parts of the eastern and central United States. Several broods of Periodical Cicadas emerge in cycles of 13 or 17 years in different regions. One such brood is found in northern Texas, mostly along the Red River, but Periodical Cicadas are not found in central Texas. Their coordinated emergence ensures that more cicadas are above ground than can be eaten by their predators, which leaves plenty of cicadas to reproduce successfully. Because they appear only once every 13 or 17 years (depending on the brood), predator populations cannot easily track their emergence, and so many more cicadas survive in these mass appearances to reproduce.

This brings up several interesting questions: how are cicadas noting the passing of years while buried several feet underground? How can a cicada count to 13 or 17? Why are their life cycles based on such odd numbers? The answer to the first question is that the cicadas are responding to the seasonal physiological changes in the roots that they feed upon. The answers to the second and third questions are just now becoming clearer, although they are not yet fully explained.

Some biologists have noted that 13 and 17 are prime numbers (evenly divisible only by themselves and one), and many have hypothesized that life cycles based on prime numbers might be especially difficult for potential predators to track. That might explain why 13- or 17-year life cycles are advantageous, but it doesn't explain how such life cycles might have arisen in the first place, or how cicadas might know when 13 or 17 years have passed.

It now appears that the first year of a cicada's life is spent on the initial hatching and life stage, or instar. After that, subsequent instars require, on average, four years to develop. The Periodical Cicadas typically require at least three of these four-year life stages, although in some northern areas, they usually require an additional four-year stage. Thus, the time to emergence for most Periodical Cicadas is either 1 year + (3 x 4 years) = 13 years or 1 year + (4 x 4 years) = 17 years, depending on local conditions and the cicadas' genetic makeup. Less common intervals of 9 years (with only two 4-year instars) and 21 years (with five 4-year instars) are known as well. Ongoing studies are addressing whether and how populations of cicadas may coordinate their emergence on 13- or 17-year cycles.

Meanwhile, in central Texas, substantial (but not overwhelming) numbers of Dog-Day Cicadas emerge every summer. Listen carefully to the cicadas singing from different oak trees around central Texas, and you will likely hear the songs of several different species. The more you listen and learn, the more you may start to associate this time of year with the Dog-Day Cicada songs of summer.

29

Going Batty

⋀ Mexican Free-tailed Bats emerging from the James River Bat Cave.

Halloween is symbolized by all kinds of things that are supposed to be scary or spooky. That often includes bats, although how these lovable, cute, beneficial flying wonders were ever considered scary is beyond my comprehension.

The Hill Country is home to about a dozen species of bats. Most of our bats are rarely seen by the average citizen, even though there are thousands of times as many bats as people across the Hill Country. In fact, the population of Mexican Free-tailed Bats, our most abundant species, in just one tiny cave in Mason County is a thousand times the number of humans in the entire county.

That tiny cave, in the Eckert James River Bat Cave Preserve

(owned and managed by The Nature Conservancy), is one of the best places anywhere to observe a nightly bat emergence. During the summer months, the cave is a maternity ward filled with between 4 million and 6 million Mexican Free-tailed Bats. Females come here in May to give birth and raise their single offspring. They stay through September, and then most return to tropical Mexico in October.

Each night, the mother bats leave the cave to feed; this is when most people get to witness their magnificent flight. Shortly after sunset on most nights, the adults begin to emerge for their nocturnal feeding. It often takes an hour or so for millions of bats to emerge from the cave. The morning return, when the bats reenter the cave, is at least as exciting to watch, although compared with the evening emergence, many fewer people witness the morning event.

Visitors to the cave get to watch the emergence from a perch immediately above the entrance—so close that they can feel the rush of the bats as they swirl by on their exit flight. Humans are not the only species that comes to watch the emergence. Hawks, owls, snakes, and other predators are often there as well, waiting to grab a bat or two as they make their way from the cave.

Witnessing this bat emergence against the red skies of a summer sunset is one of the most moving nature phenomena that one can experience in the Texas Hill Country. Many people describe the emergence as a "bat tornado." The acrobatics, agility, and coordination needed for several million bats to fly out of a tiny cave opening are hard to believe. Can you imagine several million airplanes trying to take off at once from the same runway? It would be a complete disaster. In the case of the bats, collisions are rare, and almost all the bats emerge without serious incident.

Those millions of bats are extremely important to both the ecology and economy of the surrounding Hill Country. Each night, each bat eats close to its body weight in insects, meaning that bats are responsible for the population control of numerous agricultural and human pests, including mosquitoes, cutworm moths, and corn-borer moths. That's hundreds of millions of insect pests eaten every night of the summer, just by the bats from a single Hill Country cave.

As I've noted, the James River Bat Cave is a maternal colony, so only female bats and their offspring roost there. The male bats do not require the same constant temperature and humidity conditions needed by the nursing mothers, so the males roost in much more varied locations. Each mother bat in the maternity colony gives birth to a single pup, from late June to early July. The young grow quickly and are able to fly by mid- to late August, when they begin joining their mothers in nightly foraging trips. Therefore, the largest flights are typically late in the summer, when both mothers and young emerge from the cave to feed.

By late October, most of the bats have left for the winter to spend the colder months in Mexico, where they can still find flying insects for meals. The females will also breed there the next spring, and they will be pregnant with another pup when they return to the Hill Country in May. Females can live up to 18 years, and they produce another pup each year. Of course, many bats do not survive, as they have many predators. They can succumb as well to disease and, increasingly, to poisoning from insecticides.

Biologists are still learning many aspects of the complex biology of bats. Imagine 4 million or so mother bats returning to their roost after a night of foraging. First, they must negotiate their reentry to the cave, without colliding with any of the millions of other bats making their way back in. Then, each mother must find her own offspring among the millions of baby bats in the maternity ward. Each mother does locate her own pup, using a combination of cues that include scent and the sound of the bat's voices. Each mother imprints her scent on her own offspring, then finds the pup among the masses and nurses it daily.

Bats roost in many other places across the Hill Country as well, including rock outcrops, bridges, tree cavities, and buildings. You can attract bats to your yard by constructing bat houses, which provide the appropriately spaced slits that bats prefer in their roost sites. Attracting bats to your yard allows you to enjoy watching a nightly bat emergence (although at a much smaller scale than at a bat cave) and gives you the benefit of nocturnal flying insect removal. You can also take pleasure in contributing to the survival and success of one of the Hill Country's most fascinating and beneficial native residents.

30

Deer Densities on the Edwards Plateau

ʎ A Whitetail doe with her twin fawns.

There are a lot of White-tailed Deer in Texas—about 5.6 million of them. In part, that is because Texas has a lot of deer habitat. If we exclude areas of west Texas where Whitetails do not occur, there are about 113 million acres of suitable habitat in Texas, and that works out to an average density of about one Whitetail for every 20 acres of range in Texas.

Whitetails are not equally abundant across the Lone Star State, however. The Edwards Plateau Ecological Region alone supports 2.3 million Whitetails, or about 41 percent of the state total. Across the Plateau, the average is about one Whitetail for every 7 acres.

Even in the Edwards Plateau ecoregion, Whitetails are not evenly distributed. The Texas Parks and Wildlife Department divides the Plateau into five deer management units. The Central Texas Mineral Region (Llano Uplift) is one of those management units. It consists of Llano County, most of Mason County, and smaller parts of the surrounding counties. No one who is familiar with deer populations in this region will be surprised to learn that deer densities are far higher here—a deer for every 3 to 4 acres—than in any other management unit in the state. That means that the number of White-tailed Deer in Mason County, where the Double Helix Ranch is located, is about 45 times the number of humans.

Why are deer so abundant across the Llano Uplift, and to a lesser extent, throughout the Edwards Plateau ecoregion? The first reason is habitat. The White-tailed Deer is often described as an edge species, which means that it prefers open woodlands over closed-canopy forests or grasslands. In parts of the state, the best deer habitat occurs at the edges of forests, where there is enough sunlight for broad-leaved forbs and other preferred foods to grow. In contrast, the open woodlands of the Llano Uplift represent nearly continuous, almost ideal Whitetail habitat. Deer need woody vegetation to use as cover for protection from predators, and they also need woody browse as another major part of their diet. Finally, they thrive on mast (fruits and nuts), especially in the late summer and fall. These three major components of a deer's diet—forbs, woody browse, and mast—are all abundant throughout the Llano Uplift, as is appropriate escape cover.

Mast production in the Llano Uplift is enormous, providing a critical pre-winter boost to the deer herd. Acorns from the abundant oak trees are a major part of this boost, but several other plants provide large mast crops in our area as well. In the late summer, the fruits from Prickly Pear, Texas Persimmon, and Mustang Grape are important deer foods. Other local trees that produce important mast crops for deer include Pecan, Netleaf Hackberry, and Yaupon.

The Llano Uplift also supports green-leaved woody browse throughout the year. Even in the winter, the Plateau Live Oaks remain green, and Mistletoe (another favorite deer food) is abundant. In addition, the mild climate allows forbs to sprout in the fall and remain green throughout the winter. Winter is a stress season in many deer populations, but it is not typically very stressful for central Texas Whitetails, as they have access to green vegetation throughout the cold season.

Hill Country deer populations have always been higher than the state average, but deer populations have grown dramatically across Texas (and elsewhere in the United States) over the last century. The elimination of screwworm flies across central and southern Texas in the 1950s and 1960s was a big reason for this population boom. Before their elimination, screwworm flies contributed to high deer mortality by laying their eggs in open wounds. The screwworm infection would then weaken and often kill the host.

Subsistence hunting during and after the Great Depression of the 1930s led to increased human harvests of deer in the first half of the twentieth century. Populations of Pumas, Wolves, and other traditional predators of deer were depleted in the late 1800s and early 1900s. As a result, deer populations are now largely controlled by human predators and road mortality, and in many areas of the Llano Uplift, we are no longer harvesting enough deer to control their expanding populations. Management strategies now focus on taking enough does to keep the population in check. Buck harvests have a much smaller effect, as population growth is largely limited by the number of females (as one buck can impregnate many does).

When deer populations were lower in the first half of the 1900s, legal deer harvest was limited to bucks. Protection of does allowed the deer population to grow rapidly, but it also created a lasting culture of buck-only harvest. Now that our deer populations are at or above the long-term carrying capacity of the land, the emphasis has shifted to harvesting at least as many does as bucks. This change in management strategies has resulted in more even and natural buck to doe ratios, and bucks are living longer and growing larger than they did under a buck-only management system.

The Llano Uplift has long been recognized as the Deer Capital of Texas. Its deer populations are larger and healthier than they have been in any recent era. The biggest potential threat to Texas deer populations is the introduction of a serious disease, such as chronic wasting disease. This disease has been detected in parts of the Edwards Plateau, having arrived via the introduction of captive-bred deer. So far, it has not yet spread to the Llano Uplift, and testing and regulation of captive deer herds might keep it from spreading. Other than disease, our biggest problem is overpopulation, which represents a potential for exceeding the carrying capacity of the land. One of our biggest management challenges on the Double Helix Ranch is harvesting enough deer to keep the population healthy. But with proper management, this is a golden age for deer populations in central Texas.

31

Bucks in Velvet

⋏ A White-tailed Deer buck in velvet, at a water hole.

Many people ask me about "velvet bucks"—also known as cactus bucks or (incorrectly) as stag bucks. Those are all names sometimes used to refer to bucks that don't shed the velvet on their antlers in the fall. Such bucks are found occasionally throughout the range of the White-tailed Deer, but they occur at a relatively high frequency in the Llano Uplift area of the Hill Country. Why are they found more often in this particular area?

Normally, bucks shed their velvet in our area at the end of August or beginning of September, as the days of summer begin to shorten. The decreasing photoperiod stimulates an increase in testosterone production in normal bucks, and the elevated testosterone levels stimulate numerous physiological changes. Blood flow to the living tissue of the antlers is cut off, the velvet is shed, and the deer rubs the antlers clean. In addition, the buck's neck thickens, and he begins to make scrapes and rubs, all in anticipation of the upcoming breeding season.

If a buck does not produce adequate testosterone, then none of those changes occur. The antlers may continue to grow and remain in velvet. If the testosterone levels are very low, the antlers will not even be shed at the end of the season, and they may then form an unusual shape over time. Such retained antlers often take on a knobby, cactuslike appearance with many abnormal points, which leads many people to call bucks with such antlers "cactus bucks."

The technical term for such animals is cryptorchid bucks. They have seriously underdeveloped testicles that may not even descend into the scrotum. They are not reproductive, and they do not participate in the usual seasonal changes of reproductive behavior typical of other bucks. They may grow quite heavy, as they don't dedicate their activity to reproduction during the rut.

Cryptorchidism can result from a birth defect or from an injury to the testicles (from jumping over a fence, for example). That is the usual way that velvet bucks occur throughout the Whitetail range. But why are bucks in velvet during the breeding season so much more common in the Llano Uplift area? Also, most of our late-season bucks in velvet are not actually cactus bucks, because they have relatively normal-looking antlers that are not retained at the end of the season but eventually shed. These bucks simply retain their antlers in velvet into the fall, and do not participate in rutting and breeding activities.

Many plants are known to produce compounds called phyto-estrogens—chemicals that mimic or modulate the action of vertebrate hormones. In addition, agricultural chemicals such as herbicides and pesticides include many xenoestrogens that can also disrupt vertebrate hormonal cycles. Either of those sources of estrogen-like compounds can disrupt normal reproductive patterns of the White-tailed Deer, resulting in reduced testicles and lower than normal testosterone production. Testosterone production may be reduced enough to retain velvet on the antlers and to prevent bucks from participating in the fall rut and breeding season.

Although the local source of estrogen-like compounds in the diet of our Whitetails is still under study, the year-to-year frequency of velvet bucks gives us some clues. The frequency of fall bucks in velvet increases in and follows drought years, especially if dry conditions are punctuated by brief, late-summer rains. Biologists think that certain plants that are common on the Llano Uplift—plants that tend to green up suddenly in a dry period after rain—are the most likely candidates. One such group of plants includes the spikemosses—the low mats of plants that grow abundantly on the shallow, rocky, granitic soils of the Llano Uplift, especially in areas of granite or gneiss outcrops. They are sometimes called resurrection plants, because they quickly change from a dried appearance to a green, vibrant form after summer rains. They may not be the only or primary source of phytoestrogens in the diet of our deer, but they are one of the major suspects.

Deer are attracted to green vegetation, and spikemosses contain high levels of phytoestrogens. If an otherwise normal buck eats large quantities of spikemoss when it greens up in the summer, the buck's endocrine cycle may be disrupted. If testosterone levels do not rise sufficiently at the end of the summer, the buck will not shed its velvet, and the velvet antlers will be retained into the fall. Also, if does eat the phytoestrogens, their fawns may be the most likely to be affected as they mature into bucks.

Although cryptorchid bucks do not participate in typical reproductive behavior, there is no danger to humans in consuming these animals. The animals are typically in excellent body condition, as they are not worn down by the strains of rutting and breeding. Many managers recommend that hunters take cryptorchid bucks as part of their management program, since they do not contribute to the future gene pool of the deer population.

32

The Future of Hill Country Deer Populations

⅄ A Whitetail buck on a sunny fall morning.

White-tailed Deer are a critical part of the Hill Country's economy and culture. Many landowners rely on income from deer leases, and deer hunters and their families represent a significant fraction of visitors to the Hill Country. Lots of local businesses rely on deer season to stay in the black each year. Venison from harvested deer is an important and preferred source of food for local residents, and deer camps are a center of social activity and interactions for many Hill Country residents each fall. Overall, the local economic impact of deer is higher than that of any agricultural crop or other product produced on the Edwards Plateau. Statewide, deer hunting contributes $2.2 billion to the Texas economy every year.

Beyond human economic and social interests, deer play an important role in our local ecosystem. If deer are excluded from an area, the changes in the vegetation are quite dramatic. Deer help keep our woodlands open, which is important for many of the other native plants and animals in the Hill Country. Some potentially problematic plant species, such as poison ivy, are not currently a major local problem because they are kept in check by deer browsing. On the other hand, our deer populations are currently too high for recruitment of some key species (such as some of our local oaks and other trees).

Hill Country deer populations are as large and generally as healthy as they have ever been. The primary challenge with current deer management is harvesting enough deer (especially does) each year to keep the population from exceeding the carrying capacity of the land, thereby allowing populations of our native plants to flourish. We just don't have enough deer predators left to keep the populations in check without intensive hunting.

To help control the high deer populations, many informed deer managers and landowners now support our occasional deer predators, such as Coyotes, Bobcats, and the few remaining Mountain Lions. Deer are not a major component of the diet of Coyotes or Bobcats, although both do take deer opportunistically (especially fawns). Most ranches in the Hill Country simply do not harvest enough deer through human hunting to keep the deer herds below carrying capacity. The larger predators are also critical for controlling populations of raccoons and other mid-sized predators (termed mesopredators), whose populations have exploded in recent years. High raccoon populations, in turn, have depressed many species of birds (especially ground-nesting species such as our quail, the Bobwhite, and the Wild Turkey), as well as populations of other small vertebrates, such as frogs and lizards.

Besides overpopulation, other factors pose a potential threat to the future of deer populations. The biggest looming threat is chronic wasting disease, a prion disease that is easily transmitted from one infected deer to another. It leads to emaciation, changes in behavior, and eventually death of the deer. A prion is a form of a protein that can trigger normal proteins to fold incorrectly, especially in the central nervous system, including the brain.

To understand a prion, think of an origami figure, beautifully folded into a swan. If you have good instructions, or a good example to use as a model, you can take a new piece of paper and fold a new swan. But if someone gives you a flawed example, and you use that as a model, all of your new origami swans will be flawed. Similarly, prions are incorrectly folded proteins that can influence the folding of new proteins. Unfortunately, a misfolded protein may not function as it should, and that can lead to serious disease.

Several prion diseases are known to cause neurological dysfunction and death in mammals. Perhaps the most infamous prion disease is bovine spongiform encephalopathy (or mad cow disease), which decimated the cattle industry in the United Kingdom in the 1980s and 1990s. The prion responsible for mad cow disease can also result in a rare but serious human ailment—a variant of Creutzfeldt–Jakob disease that can lead to brain degeneration and death. In contrast, there are no known cases in which the prion that causes chronic wasting disease in deer has resulted in human disease, although transmission from deer to other species is possible. Hence, the eating of deer that are infected with chronic wasting disease is not recommended.

Chronic wasting disease was first detected in captive Mule Deer herds in Colorado in 1967. It is thought that the disease may have originated from a related prion disease in sheep known as scrapie. For many years, chronic wasting disease was limited in wild deer to an area of Colorado and Wyoming. In recent decades, it has been spread around the United States, especially through the transport of captive deer. As of this writing, captive deer breeding operations have transmitted the disease to 26 states, including Texas. When captive-bred deer are released into the wild, they can quickly infect the local wild deer populations, and the infection spreads.

The first case of chronic wasting disease in Texas deer was reported in 2012, in a Mule Deer from the Trans-Pecos region. The disease has since been spread to five areas of the state, in each case the result of transport of captive deer. In an effort to constrain the disease, the Texas Parks and Wildlife Department has established five containment areas in places where the disease has been detected. The department also monitors deer killed in other areas of the state to look for new areas of infection. Deer harvested in containment zones are required to be tested for chronic wasting disease at check stations in each containment area. No animal or animal parts (including meat) can be removed from a containment area until the harvested deer has been cleared as free from chronic wasting disease.

Hill Country residents and visitors need to be aware of chronic wasting disease, and they should report any sick deer immediately to the Texas Parks and Wildlife Department. Signs of infection include emaciation, lack of muscle coordination, staggering with the head and ears lowered, or an excessively shaggy coat. Even if harvested deer appear to be healthy and you wish to test a deer for chronic wasting disease, contact your local Texas Parks and Wildlife biologist.

Once chronic wasting disease is established in an area, it is virtually impossible to eliminate. It is critical for landowners and hunters to be aware of the disease and to work to contain it. Our deer populations, and the future of deer hunting, depend on it.

33

The Carbon Cycle and How It Affects Our Daily Lives

⋏ Gorman Falls at Colorado Bend State Park. The calcium carbonate flowstone represents one of the stable reservoirs of carbonate rock in the Earth's surface.

You have undoubtedly heard people discussing ways to reduce our carbon footprint, and the concerns about increasing levels of carbon dioxide in the Earth's atmosphere. But the total amount of carbon on Earth is not changing. What is changing is where the carbon is located. Like other elements, carbon is cycled through different forms (different chemical compounds) by both natural and human-mediated processes.

Living organisms and their remains are largely composed of

compounds that we call organic carbon. These carbon compounds are produced through photosynthesis by plants, which take carbon dioxide from the atmosphere, combine it with water, produce carbohydrates (sugars), and release oxygen into the atmosphere as a by-product. Plants then use those sugars as building blocks and energy sources to build all the other organic compounds that make up a plant. Animals then eat the plants (or eat other animals that eat plants) and use the organic compounds for their own bodies and metabolism.

When a plant or animal uses some of those carbon compounds to support its metabolism, it reverses the process, and converts some of the carbohydrates back into carbon dioxide, while extracting oxygen from the atmosphere. When the organism dies, it typically decomposes (through the action of bacteria and other decomposers), and most of the carbon in the organic compounds that make up its body are returned to the atmosphere as carbon dioxide.

Over long periods of time, however, some carbon from deceased organisms can be trapped underground, in environments where the oxygen supply is limited and decay is thus halted. Over many millions of years, those organic remains can accumulate. The resulting deposits are known as fossil fuels—coal, oil, and natural gas—because they are derived from the remains of once-living organisms. Coal deposits are largely remains of plants that were deposited in oxygen-depleted environments, such as swamps. Oil and natural gas are mostly formed from the remains of algae that accumulate at the bottom of oceans. The deposits take tens of millions to hundreds of millions of years to form. When we burn fossil fuels, we quickly release the carbon that accumulated over millions of years back into the atmosphere.

When we talk about our carbon footprint, we are talking about human actions that move carbon from the soil and from deep underground (fossil fuels) into the atmosphere, in the form of carbon dioxide. Atmospheric carbon dioxide levels have been steadily accumulating in the Earth's atmosphere since the Industrial Revolution, especially since the extensive use of fossil fuels began. In addition, changes to the land (replacing forests and grasslands with intensive agriculture, for example, as well as the production of concrete) have also released large quantities of carbon dioxide into the atmosphere. About two-thirds of the global increases in carbon dioxide over the past century have resulted from the burning of fossil fuels, and about one-third from changing land use.

Increasing atmospheric levels of carbon dioxide are a concern because this gas (as well as other greenhouse gases produced from burning or releasing fossil fuels, such as methane) traps energy from sunlight, acting like a greenhouse to hold the heat near the Earth's surface. More carbon dioxide in the atmosphere results in changes to the Earth's climate. Those changes are having large negative consequences for the environment of the Earth, and for the lives of its human populations.

Most of Earth's carbon is tied up in relatively stable rock formations, such as limestone, and in inorganic carbon compounds that are dissolved in the oceans. Large amounts of the total supply of organic carbon compounds are stored in stable geological deposits of fossil fuels (stable, at least, until we extract and burn them). Where is the rest of the organic carbon, which serves as a potential source for atmospheric carbon dioxide, located? The amount of carbon stored in living plants and animals (about 560 gigatons) is actually less than the amount of atmospheric carbon (about 800 gigatons), but both of these carbon reservoirs are relatively small compared with the carbon that is stored in the shallow surface soils of the Earth—about 1,550 gigatons of organic carbon, and another 950 gigatons of inorganic carbon (elemental carbon and carbonate minerals).

If carbon dioxide continues to accumulate in Earth's atmosphere at the present rate, the climatic changes that will result are expected to be catastrophic. Polar ice caps over landmasses are already melting, and if that continues, it will result in a rise in sea level and significant flooding of coastal cities. Climates everywhere on the Earth will change dramatically, with enormous consequences for agricultural production, biodiversity, immigration, and, likely, political stability. These changes are not in the far-distant future. They are beginning to happen now and will be severe within a single human generation—unless, of course, we take immediate action, and begin to reverse the accumulation of carbon dioxide in the atmosphere.

There are ways that we can reduce both of the large sources of new atmospheric greenhouse gases like carbon dioxide (from fossil fuels and from changing land use). If we reduce the production of these gases and begin to sequester some of the carbon back into terrestrial reservoirs (in forests, grasslands, topsoil, or even deep underground), we can slow or possibly even reverse atmospheric carbon accumulation. That will require a transition from fossil fuels to sustainable energy sources, and it will also require a change in agricultural practices to methods that replenish, rather than remove, the organic matter in our soils. Many of these changes can benefit agriculture in other ways, including reducing the costs associated with inorganic fertilizers and fossil-fuel use.

The changes that we will need to make over the coming decades are great, but they are doable. Changes in what we do and how we live may seem hard at first, but they are tiny compared with the climatic changes that will occur if we don't take immediate and sustained action.

Open outcrops of 1.1-billion-year-old Valley Springs Gneiss (in the foreground) give way to oak-covered hills composed of Hickory Sandstone. ➤

VI

BACKYARD BIOLOGY

Even if you are not a landowner, there is a great deal of biodiversity that you can observe in your own back yard or city park. If you have a house or apartment with a garden, planting native plants and creating natural cover and habitat can attract a wide diversity of interesting native animals. A small pool of water (not chlorinated) can attract frogs, birds, dragonflies, and other wildlife. Bird feeders, providing sugar water, seeds, suet, fruit, and nuts, bring a myriad of birds through the seasons. Native plants that produce flowers and berries are also magnets for many butterflies and birds. Simple rock piles can serve as protective homes for frogs, toads, and lizards.

◄ Eastern Gamagrass growing by a backyard pool on the Double Helix Ranch. Even small pools of water can attract many animals for easy viewing.

Rather than trying to sterilize your back yard with insecticides and high-maintenance lawn grass, you may find great enjoyment in attracting and observing some of our fascinating insects and other native animals. Most of our native Texas ants are not human pests, and few will bite or sting unless strongly provoked. Many insects also provide important ecological services, so a healthy garden is also a diverse garden. Far from a sign of trouble, a diverse community of insects in your garden is a sign of a healthy, functioning ecosystem.

If you seek out the smaller and less conspicuous life forms in your back yard, you may be surprised at what you find. Few people take the time to look closely at the intricate beauty of lichens, for example. Once you do, and you understand the complexity of their cooperative lives, you may never stop marveling at them.

34

The Remarkable Life of Hummingbirds

⋀ Black-chinned Hummingbirds crowding around a hummingbird feeder at dusk on the Double Helix Ranch.

Across the Hill Country, feeders filled with sugar water are likely to attract lots of Black-chinned and Ruby-throated hummingbirds. You may even be lucky enough to spot one of our rarer migrants of the Hill Country, such as a Rufous or Calliope hummingbird. Whichever species of hummer I encounter, it is usually the hum of their rapid flight that first catches my attention.

That sound never fails to bring a smile to my face, as I recall the joy I've experienced watching and listening to hummers from the shade of our front porch.

Our only regular nesting summer hummer is the Black-chinned Hummingbird, which is abundant locally. The birds arrive in our area in early to mid-March, and most of the adults have flown south by late summer, although the young often stay until early fall. Ruby-throated Hummingbirds are also common here as they migrate through in the spring and fall, but they mostly nest to our north and east. In the late summer and early fall, most of our hummers are young-of-the-year Black-chinned Hummingbirds that haven't yet migrated, or Ruby-throated Hummingbirds passing through on their way south.

Most people think of hummingbirds largely as nectar feeders, as we typically see them feeding at flowers or hummingbird feeders. They do get lots of energy from nectar to support their active lifestyle, but hummingbirds can't survive on a diet of only sugar. They also need protein, which they get by consuming large numbers of small insects and other invertebrates. Typical prey of hummers includes spiders, beetles, aphids, ants, mosquitoes, gnats, and other small flies.

Hummingbirds construct their tiny nests out of plant fibers, small twigs, pieces of leaves, and bits of lichen, all carefully woven together with spider silk. They will gather wood ash and lichens to cover their nests, which make them frustratingly hard to spot in the branches of trees and shrubs. Even though hummingbird nests are common in the trees around our homes, they are rarely seen, as they usually look like little more than a bump on a branch from below, and they are often covered by a canopy of leaves from above. If you search carefully in trees, you might spot one of these lichen-covered marvels of engineering 10 feet or more off the ground, often in the fork of a branch.

A hummingbird egg is about the size of a pinto bean, and females typically lay two in a nest. They are then incubated for 15 to 18 days before they hatch. Female hummingbirds handle all the care of the young, which they feed by regurgitating insects and nectar into the tiny nestlings' beaks. The young grow rapidly, and the nest, thanks to the spider silk, is actually elastic enough that it expands to accommodate the growing nestlings. By 18 to 28 days after hatching, the young have developed enough to fledge the nest and begin feeding on their own.

Relative to body weight, the hummingbird brain is the largest of any bird's (about 4.2 percent of the hummer's body weight), although the absolute size of the brain is tiny (about 0.005 of an ounce for a Black-chinned Hummingbird). Hummers have excellent memories for the locations of flowers and other food sources they have visited. Their relatively large brains are also needed to control their remarkable flying skills, as they are the only birds that can fly straight up, down, sideways, and even backward—in addition to forward, of course. Although we typically see hummers as they hover in midair to feed on nectar from a flower or feeder, they can fly at about 25 to 30 miles per hour, even reaching speeds of about 50 miles per hour in a dive.

Each year, our hummingbirds must migrate to tropical parts of Mexico or Central America for the winter, where they can still find abundant flowers and insects for their diet. Our Black-chinned Hummingbirds mostly fly overland to Mexico, whereas many Ruby-throated Hummingbirds fly long distances across the Gulf of Mexico to reach Central America (especially on their northward flight; more individuals seem to fly along the coast when heading south). To make this nonstop flight of about 500 miles, they need to build up fat deposits by eating lots of spiders and insects. They double their body weight before migration and then lose about 60 percent of their preflight weight in making the long journey across the water. Moving north, hummers need to time their trip with the appearance of spring blossoms and insect hatches, as they will arrive nearly exhausted and must depend on available nectar and abundant insects for survival. Once they reach land, they continue moving north at about 20 miles a day, advancing with spring as flowers start to bloom. Hummingbirds return year after year to the same place they hatched; they live an average of about five years (although a few individuals can live up to a decade).

When they are active, hummingbirds have a very high metabolic rate and body temperature. In this state, they must feed constantly or they will rapidly lose body weight (as they do in long-distance migration). To conserve energy at night or in cold weather, hummingbirds can enter a state called torpor. They lock their feet on a perch, lower their body temperature, slow their heart rate to just a few beats per minute, and appear to be unconscious. While in torpor, they may even get knocked over and appear to be hanging upside down, but with their feet still clamped tightly on a perch. If you see a hummingbird in this state, leave it alone. It is not dead or injured, and it will recover and fly off when the conditions are favorable.

Hummingbirds are easy to attract to your yard and fascinating to watch. You can attract them by planting tubular flowers that produce a lot of nectar, or with hummingbird feeders. One of their favorite flowers in our area is also a delight for gardeners—Standing Cypress. The seeds of Standing Cypress are easy to collect; they germinate readily across much of the Hill Country, and then the plant will self-seed wherever it grows well. Standing Cypress is a biennial, meaning that usually it takes two years to bloom, so you may want to seed it for two successive years to get it established.

If you want to attract hummers with feeders, just use regular table sugar to make the nectar (a ratio of one part sugar to four parts water is standard). Don't add any dyes, which are harmful to hummingbirds. Remember to clean the feeders and replace the sugar water daily, or toxic molds can grow that will harm the birds. Once the hummingbirds have left for the winter, remove and clean the feeders thoroughly, and then have them ready to fill again by mid-March.

35

Ways to Attract and Increase Bird Populations

⋀ A Painted Bunting. It is easy to attract birds to yards and gardens if the appropriate native seed plants are provided. *Photo courtesy of Bill J. Boyd Photography.*

A recent comprehensive study of North American bird populations found a drop of nearly 3 billion birds in the United States and Canada over the past 50 years. That represents a 30 percent decline in our native bird populations. The drop in birds that live and breed in grasslands has been even greater, with a decline in populations of more than half. If you were alive in the 1970s or earlier, you witnessed populations of native birds that were far greater than they are today.

What has caused these rapid declines, and is there anything that we can do to reverse this trend? We can learn some of the reasons for the losses by looking at which species have declined the most.

Also, mixed in with the overall declines are some striking success stories, and those successes point to actions that might well apply more generally.

Just 12 bird families account for over 90 percent of the losses. Especially hard-hit are birds in the sparrow, warbler, finch, lark, and blackbird families. Many migratory species are in decline as migrating birds face new and dangerous obstacles. Among the most serious of these are tall buildings that are lighted at night. The lights reflecting off windows can confuse a migrating bird, which could collide with a window and fall to its death. A study at a high-rise building in Chicago found that turning out the lights at night during bird migration reduced bird deaths by 80 percent. Now many cities are reducing or eliminating late-night lights (typically between midnight and 6 A.M.) in high-rise buildings, which is greatly reducing bird collisions and deaths. It isn't just tall buildings that are the problem, however—many birds are killed on the windows of houses as well. A simple, effective solution is to install screens on the outside of windows, which hides the reflective glass and makes bird collisions much less likely (as well as less likely to be lethal).

Losses of breeding habitat are another major reason for bird declines. Grasslands, in particular, have been lost to agriculture. Locally, many Hill Country ranchers are working to reverse this trend, as the benefits of hardy, drought-resistant native grasses are becoming better known. These native grasses require minimal input of irrigation water, fertilizers, and insecticides, so a well-managed native grassland can provide economic benefits to landowners, as well as helping to restore native wildlife. In town, reducing lawns in favor of native plants is one of the best ways to attract more birds to your yard.

Many of the birds that have declined eat mainly insects. The declines in these bird species mirror the declines in their prey populations. Some groups of insects have declined precipitously over the past half-century. If you have been driving that long, you likely know that the windshield of your car accumulates insects much more slowly than it once did. You may consider that good news, but insects are essential for pollinating our crops, and they serve as an important food base for many animals. A decline in insect populations results in a decline in birds, frogs, toads, lizards, bats, and many other insectivores.

If you wish to attract nesting birds (such as the Eastern Bluebird, a beautiful native species that readily takes to nesting boxes), then it is important not to poison their prey base. Bluebirds raise their young on a diet of insects, and they especially target caterpillars as food items. Most caterpillars, in turn, require native plants as food sources. Planting appropriate native plants attracts butterflies, whose caterpillars feed the hatchling birds (and their parents). But it is important not to use pesticides on these native plants, or the poisons will accumulate in predators of insects, such as bluebirds. Insecticide use is thus double trouble for birds, as the insecticides reduce insect populations and poison the insects that remain.

Outdoor cats kill billions of birds every year in the United States and Canada. Studies suggest that cats are the second largest reason for bird population declines, after loss of habitat. Cats can make wonderful pets, but they are efficient predators of birds, lizards, and many other small animals. More than 100 million feral and outdoor cats are estimated to live in North America alone, and each outdoor cat kills, on average, dozens of birds every year. That source of bird mortality is entirely within our control. If we keep our pet cats indoors and eliminate feral cat populations, the declines in many bird populations can be reversed. The increase in raccoon populations (which is related, at least in part, to year-round feeding of protein supplements that are intended for deer) is another large source of bird mortality, especially with regard to ground-nesting species such as the Bobwhite.

I mentioned above that not all bird populations have declined over the past half-century. Indeed, there are several success stories. The three groups of birds that have fared the best over this time are waterfowl (ducks and geese), the Wild Turkey, and many raptors (especially hawks, eagles, and falcons). These birds have bucked the overall downward trend for a variety of reasons, but there are several important takeways.

Waterfowl have benefited from concentrated efforts by conservation groups (such as Ducks Unlimited), which have worked to raise money to protect breeding habitat. Federal and state duck stamps (largely bought by waterfowl hunters) have also provided large income streams that have been used to protect critical waterfowl habitat (especially the wetlands that are used by waterfowl for breeding). As a result, waterfowl populations have increased by nearly half over the past half-century. This demonstrates that declines can be reversed with direct efforts to preserve critical wildlife habitat. Similarly, Wild Turkey populations have increased (especially in parts of the eastern United States), also through habitat improvement and better management of turkey populations, again funded largely by hunters and hunting groups, including stamps that are required for hunting upland game birds in Texas.

Raptor populations, in contrast, have benefited from laws that protect endangered species, and especially from the banning of the insecticide DDT in North America. DDT was found to accumulate in raptors through the food chain. The DDT concentration resulted in weakened eggshells and lowered reproductive success. The banning of DDT quickly reversed that trend in North American raptor populations, many of which have now recovered or are still recovering from population lows in the 1960s. Peregrine Falcons, which had been all but eliminated from Texas, now nest on the Tower on the University of Texas campus in Austin. If you visit the campus, you are likely to spot the birds as they hunt across the campus. You can also watch them on the Falcon Cam that is operated by the UT Biodiversity Center (https://biodiversity.utexas.edu).

Recent studies have found that many raptors, including Bald Eagles, are suffering from lead poisoning across North America. The lead comes from lead fragments in the remains of game animals that are scavenged by the eagles. This source of poisoning could be easily eliminated if hunters would switch from lead to nontoxic copper bullets (see chapter 50).

If many individuals take some of the simple actions described in this chapter, the combined effects can be enormous. Working together, we can help return billions of birds to the wild.

36

The Unexpected Beauty and Diversity of Lichens

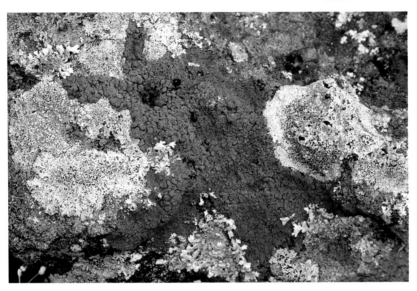

Ʌ Multicolored lichens growing on gneiss in the Llano Uplift.

The dramatic granite and gneiss outcrops of the Llano Uplift, in the middle of the Hill Country, are covered with colorful lichens, as are most of the trees that grow there. This is a great sign of our clean air, as lichens are very sensitive to air pollution. If you drive across the Hill Country from west to east, toward the large cities of Austin and San Antonio, stop and look at the oak trees along your journey. You will see that both the diversity and coverage of lichens decreases rapidly as you approach urban areas. If you continue east to Houston, you will see the lichens continue to decrease in diversity and coverage even further, as air quality declines.

The sensitivity of lichens to air pollution may seem strange, given that they live on seemingly barren surfaces, such as rocks and the bark of trees. But it makes sense when you know that lichens receive most of their nutrients and water through atmospheric deposits. Air pollution results in the depositing of high concentrations of nitrates and ammonia on lichens, which can overwhelm and kill them. Heavy metals, such as lead, also accumulate in lichens and can eventually become toxic. These attributes make lichens an excellent bioindicator of clean air—less air pollution means more diverse and abundant lichens.

Have you ever stopped to look closely at lichens and wondered what kind of organisms they are? They are puzzling because they are not just one kind of organism but rather several kinds of organisms living together in a close, interdependent relationship known as symbiosis. Most biologists consider this relationship mutualistic because the various partners all benefit from their cooperative interactions.

At minimum, a lichen consists of a symbiotic interaction between a fungus and a population of unicellular photosynthetic organisms. The photosynthetic organisms are typically algae, but they can also be cyanobacteria (a group of photosynthetic bacteria). Some lichens involve interactions among a few different species of fungi, although one of the fungi provides the primary structural home for the lichen. The fungal filaments gather and retain moisture and nutrients from the atmosphere and anchor the lichen to the surface of a rock or tree. These filaments protect the photosynthetic algal cells and provide a moist environment in which they can thrive. The algae, in turn, use photosynthesis to convert carbon dioxide and water into sugars and sugar alcohols, which are used as an energy source by both the algae and the fungus.

Biologists give lichens scientific names based on their major fungal component. The algae are named separately. In many cases, the fungus and algae are not known to live separately from one another, although the same algae may form lichens with many different species of fungi. Some fungi also form lichens with more than one photosynthetic partner. The resultant lichens may look different from one another, but because they are based on the same fungal partner, they share the same scientific name.

The growth form of lichens can be quite variable. Some of our lichens look like tiny branching bushes that bear small cup-shaped fruiting bodies. These are called fruticose lichens, and one of our most common examples in the Hill Country is the bright orange lichen that goes by the scientific name *Teloschistes exilis.* You will find this bright, beautiful, bushy, branching lichen growing mostly on trees, and it seems to especially like the dead lower branches of oak trees.

Many of our other local lichens form flat, easily removable, leaf-like structures that cover rocks or trees. Known as foliose lichens, they are especially common on tree bark. Our local species are mostly shades of green and gray. In some parts of the world, such as southwestern China, foliose lichens are eaten by humans as a local delicacy. I have enjoyed lichen dishes prepared with peppers and pork in China, although I do not recommend that you try this with our Hill Country lichens. Lichens are also used to make dyes and various types of medicinal compounds.

Most lichens that grow on rocks form a tight crust on the rock's surface, so they are known as crustose lichens. Many of our crustose lichens are bright yellow or orange, although you may find lichens in hues across the color spectrum, including black and white. These lichens are what make our local rock outcrops so colorful. The colors of lichens tend to be brightest when they are wet and actively growing, so a wet spring day is the perfect time to go out exploring local lichen diversity.

There are about 20,000 known species of lichens around the world, and they are estimated to cover about 6 to 8 percent of the Earth's land surface. Lichens are long-lived and slow growing, so the growth of lichens on rocks can be used to date when the rocks were first exposed. If you visit a cemetery, you will notice that the oldest gravestones are covered with the most luxurious growth of lichens, which then encourages the growth of mosses and other organisms. This is why lichens are known as pioneer organisms of newly exposed surfaces; they can convert a lifeless surface to a place that other organisms can then colonize. Different lichens and other organisms may compete to cover the surface of exposed rocks, and it can be fascinating to look at the interactions and competition among several species where they come into contact.

Even if you don't want to delve into the details of lichen life history, you can enjoy lichens for their beauty and diversity. A hand lens or other magnifying glass will reveal complexity and beauty that most people never take the time to notice. Look closely at the lichens growing on the rocks and trees of the Hill Country, and you will be amazed at the underappreciated beauty you will find, even in your own back yard.

37

There Is More to Mistletoe Than Kissing

⋏ A female mistletoe plant with fruits. *Photo courtesy of Bruce W. Leander.*

S prigs of mistletoe are popular decorations around Christmas. The green leaves, white berries, and a little red ribbon give us the colors of the season, and of course there is the tradition of kissing under the mistletoe. There are many stories and myths associated with the origins of this kissing tradition. Some people trace it back to the ancient Roman festival of Saturnalia, or to early Norse or Celtic cultures. Those cultures may well have used evergreen mistletoe as a winter decoration, and they certainly used it for medicinal purposes, but the kissing tradition appears to have arisen much later, in England during the 1700s. The practice was popularized in the United States beginning in 1820, with the publication of *The Sketch Book*, by Washington Irving, which described behaviors Irving had observed in his travels in England. In any case, the tradition was already well entrenched by the time the Hill Country was settled by European immigrants, and our abundant mistletoe has likely been used in local Christmas decorations ever since.

Christmas Mistletoe, *Phoradendron tomentosum*, is the species that grows abundantly in the trees across the Hill Country. It is one of 30-some species of mistletoe that occur in North America north of Mexico (there is some disagreement about exactly how many species should be recognized). There are about 1,500 species worldwide, with a concentration in the Tropics. The word "mistletoe" is used to describe any plant in the order Santalales (sandalwood and its relatives) that is hemiparasitic—meaning that it derives part of its nutrition from a host plant. Most mistletoe species also produce their own nutrition through photosynthesis, which is why they are said to be hemiparastic rather than parasitic. Oddly enough, the mistletoe-type habit has evolved independently at least five times within the order Santalales, so plants called mistletoes actually compose several relatively distantly related groups of plants.

Mistletoe seeds are spread largely by birds. Mistletoe fruits are relished by many birds, including the Cedar Waxwing, Eastern Bluebird, silky-flycatchers, thrushes, chickadees, and doves. The seeds pass through the digestive system of some of these birds and are then deposited in trees in bird droppings. The name "mistletoe" is thought to stem from the observation that the plant grows from bird droppings—"mistel" is an Anglo-Saxon word for dung, and "tan" is an Anglo-Saxon word for twig, so "mistletoe" refers to bird dung on a tree branch. In some birds, the seeds are not passed through the digestive system but are regurgitated from the crop. Many birds simply wipe the seeds off their beaks onto tree trunks after consuming the fruits. In any case, the seeds are very sticky; they stick to the tree bark, where they germinate.

When a mistletoe germinates, it sends a structure (called a haustorium) into the tissues of the host tree. The haustorium extracts water and nutrients from the host by mimicking a growing branch on the host. This robs the host tree of these nutrients and may impede growth of the branch past the location of the mistletoe attachment.

Mistletoe is widely used by many species of animals. It is toxic if consumed by humans and some pets, but it is readily eaten by deer and livestock, especially in dry winters when few other green plants are available. If you harvest mistletoe for decorations, you will find that almost all of it grows just beyond the reach of deer. Of course, it germinates lower in trees as well, and these lower plants are readily consumed by deer. Christmas Mistletoe grows in a wide range of trees, but on our ranch, it seems to grow best in Honey Mesquite.

Several species of butterflies also use Christmas Mistletoe as a host plant for their caterpillars. Several species of hairstreak butterflies rely exclusively on mistletoe for this purpose. Adult hairstreak butterflies, as well as many species of native bees, also feed on mistletoe nectar.

Christmas Mistletoe is dioecious, meaning it has separate male and female plants. The female plants are the ones that are preferred as Christmas decorations, as they are the ones that bear white berries. These fruits are also toxic to humans, so it is important to keep them out of reach of young children (and pets) that may be tempted to eat them. Fortunately, American mistletoes are not as toxic as their European counterparts, but they can cause diarrhea, nausea, and vomiting, particularly in children. Less commonly, their consumption can result in cardiac problems.

Although mistletoe slightly weakens host trees, and is sometimes viewed as a pest for commercially important or ornamental trees, it rarely reaches densities that cause problems in our area. Its importance as a food and shelter plant for many species of animals means that it is generally considered a keystone species that is part of a healthy and diverse environment. So when you see mistletoe growing in trees, enjoy the bright green foliage and white berries, look for the differences between male and female plants, and appreciate that it is providing food to a wide variety of animals.

38

The Ups and Downs of Ants

∧ A Texas Leaf-cutter Ant (*Atta texana*) carrying a flower bud back to its nest. © *Alex Wild, used by permission.*

Many people consider ants, when they think about them at all, as irritants in their lives. We may think about ants only in negative circumstances, as when they get into our food or electrical circuits, or when we get stung by fire ants while working or playing outside. But of the 300 or so species of ants in Texas, and about 12,000 species worldwide, only a very few cause problems for humans. Most of the others provide important services that help sustain stable and functioning ecosystems.

One important role that ants play is aeration of the soil. Their nests and tunnels allow both air and water to penetrate easily below the surface, providing oxygen and moisture for plant roots. That allows more water to be absorbed locally into soils and aquifers during heavy rainfall events, so less water runs off and causes downstream flooding. Without ants, soils can become compacted, and many plants will not grow efficiently. The increased water penetration is also important for aquifers, which provide water to wells and springs.

Many ants also serve as important dispersers of seeds of native plants. Some plants depend on ants to bury their seeds. When the ants decline, so too do the native plants.

Ants are also a critical food source for many other animals. The decline in Texas Horned Lizards, for example, is partly related to a corresponding decline in their principal food source, namely, Harvester Ants. Harvester Ants have declined in recent decades as a result of interactions with imported fire ants and because some of the measures that humans use to control imported fire ants kill Harvester Ants as well.

A few species of ants do cause humans problems, especially if they are in your house or yard. Most of the ants that cause us problems locally are not native species but have been introduced from elsewhere. How can we control these pesky invaders without harming our beneficial native flora and fauna?

The ant that causes us the most problems locally is the Red Imported Fire Ant, *Solenopsis invicta*. These ants did not reach the Double Helix Ranch until the late 1990s. Before that, we did have some native fire ants (other species of *Solenopsis*) in Texas, but they did not occur in such large numbers or cause the many problems associated with the Red Imported Fire Ant. This invasive ant arrived from South America, entering at the port of Mobile Bay, in the late 1930s, probably in soil used as ballast in ships. Since then, it has spread across the southern United States. It took a half-century for the ants to reach the Hill Country.

Since Red Imported Fire Ants were largely removed from their native parasites and diseases, they increased exponentially and soon outcompeted and replaced many native ant species. Their large numbers, aggressive nature, painful stings, and attraction to electrical currents caused many problems. Many people and pets react badly to the ant's painful stings, and the damage that ants cause to outdoor electrical equipment (especially well pumps and air conditioners) is extensive.

Fire ants are also attracted to wet areas, and in the early 2000s large numbers of fire ants attacked and ate almost any small animal around water bodies on the Double Helix Ranch. Almost all emerging frogs and toads were killed by fire ants, and several species of frogs and toads disappeared or severely declined at the time. Many other species of animals were also eliminated or reduced. Populations of the Bobwhite and other ground-nesting species declined, both because of loss of food resources and as a result of direct attacks of imported fire ants on hatchlings. You may not miss some of the species eliminated by imported fire ants—longtime residents in eastern parts of the Hill Country have probably noticed that we rarely see ticks anymore, especially compared with the 1990s or earlier. That is because imported fire ants virtually eliminated ticks from large swaths of the Hill Country, along with countless numbers of beneficial species.

Unfortunately, many people reacted to the real problems of imported fire ants by broadcasting ant poisons around their homes, yards, and ranches. The poisons are indiscriminate, killing both beneficial and harmful imported species of ants. The treatments are also short-lived, and then the imported fire ants return in greater numbers because they have virtually no remaining competition from native ants. Thus, this approach generally results in larger imported fire ant populations, which then require more treatments, and the cycle continues. This is great business for the companies that sell ant poisons, but it is expensive and counterproductive for the rest of us.

A longer-term and more effective solution to the imported fire ant problem is to use biological control. Biologists at the University of Texas found that several species of tiny phorid flies were highly specific parasites of imported fire ants. The presence of the flies changed the behavior of the ants; the ants became less active in daylight hours, when the flies were active. The ants lost much of their competitive advantage, and populations declined. Imported fire ants are still present in our area, but their populations are far lower than they were 20 years ago, shortly after they arrived. We are now seeing the recovery of some native species that were nearly wiped out in the initial wave of imported fire ants.

If you have mounds of imported fire ants around your home or garden or near outdoor electrical equipment, you will likely want to eliminate them. First, make sure that the ants are actually the problematic invasive species. Once you have identified the ants, how can you kill the colony without using harmful and expensive ant poisons? One simple and inexpensive way to do this is to pour a pot of boiling water into the nest. This will kill the ants, their eggs, and the queen, and the colony will die as a result. The water will kill only the targeted ant colony and will not hurt other species away from the mound. This is by far the most effective and least expensive way to control imported fire ants around your home, and it is much less damaging to nontarget beneficial species.

39

A Pattern in the Web

⅄ The zigzag stabilimentum in the web of a Yellow Garden Spider. Whatever its actual function, the zigzag pattern makes the web more visible. *Photo courtesy of Bill J. Boyd Photography.*

The large and distinctive black and yellow spiders so common in gardens and back yards of the Hill Country go by many common names: Yellow Garden Spider, Zipper Spider, Zigzag Spider, and Writing Spider are often used. Biologists know them as *Argiope aurantia*, which translates as "gilded silver-face." Their large size, bright coloration, and distinctive webs make them among our most obvious and well-known local arachnids. The names Zigzag Spider, Zipper Spider, and Writing Spider all refer not to the coloration of the spider itself but to the distinctive zigzag design that the spiders make in their conspicuous webs. I am commonly asked why the spiders spin these strange patterns in their webs. Biologists have several ideas about the function of this structure, but it remains an open question.

The zigzag pattern is known as a web decoration, or a stabilimentum. The latter technical term was derived from the idea that the structure stabilizes the spider's web. That hypothesis has largely been discarded, however, as the structure does not seem to serve a structural purpose. The stabilimentum is only loosely attached to the rest of the web, and webs with and without the structure do not differ significantly in their stability or durability.

There are actually many distinct web designs built by orb-weaver spiders of different species. In addition to the pattern produced by our locally abundant Zigzag Spider, other related spiders build x-shaped structures, spirals, or other conspicuous designs into the center of their webs. The designs are thought to be the inspiration for E. B. White's popular children's book *Charlotte's Web*.

If not for structural stability, then why do spiders make these designs? One idea is that the designs make the spiders appear larger, which might deter potential spider predators. Another idea is that the web decorations help to camouflage the spider, or distract predators from the spider itself.

The web decorations might also function to make the spider webs more visible to birds. Why would the spiders want to do this? Birds flying through the web cause considerable damage. If the webs are more visible, birds may be more likely to avoid them, and spiders would have to make fewer repairs to their webs. Some studies have provided limited support for this hypothesis. I've certainly noticed that a web with a stabilimentum is more visible to me and makes me less likely to run into it, especially when I'm walking around the ranch at night.

The function of the web is to catch insects, so anything that makes the web attractive to potential prey (luring them in) would also be an advantage. The web decorations have been found to reflect ultraviolet light, a portion of the light spectrum that is attractive to many insects. There is little evidence, however, that webs with decorations attract any more prey than those that lack them, and some studies actually support the opposite conclusion.

The other major hypothesis about web decorations is that they attract mates. There is some limited evidence that males are more likely to be found in the webs of the large females (of at least some species related to Zigzag Spiders) when web decorations are present. Similar data are lacking for most species of orb-weaver spiders, however, or else no correlation with mate attraction has been found.

It could be that different species of spiders build web decorations for different reasons, or that some combination of factors makes the web decorations advantageous. The primary functions of the web decorations may differ under different conditions of prey and predator abundance, or competition for mates. At this point, the explanations for web decorations remain highly controversial among spider biologists.

This is an excellent example of an open scientific question about the natural history of an abundant local Hill Country species. An observant amateur naturalist, especially one willing to design a clever experiment that distinguished among hypotheses, could make an important scientific contribution by investigating these ideas. There is much we still don't know, even about common species in our own back yards.

40

Caterpillar Plagues and Their Connection to the Weather

ʎ Mesquite Loopers denuding a mesquite tree.

I n 2021, we experienced an unusually hard winter and spring, with a record late-winter cold snap, devastating April hailstorms, and a wet, cool spring. As a result of this unusual weather, I watched trees put out three separate sets of leaves, and also observed trees that didn't leaf out at all until June.

First, a hard late-February freeze set back leaf-out of many trees. Then, by early April, the Oak Leafrollers (the larvae of a small, half-inch-long moth) had denuded many oak trees, especially Post

Oaks. The caterpillars spin a thread of silk and are often found hanging by these silk strands under oak trees after they are dislodged from leaves and branches. Any time I walked under our oak trees in early April, I would get covered with Oak Leafrollers and their silk strands.

On April 12, the first of three violent hailstorms struck the Double Helix Ranch. The three-inch hailstones pummeled the ranch for more than 20 minutes, stripping virtually all trees of their leaves and small branches. With no leaves left to eat, the Oak Leafrollers quickly disappeared.

It was several weeks before the first trees began to recover and set out new leaves. Mesquite trees were among the first to recover, putting out their second set of fresh, new green leaves for the year. But that new green was short-lived, as a new plague of caterpillars soon stripped the mesquites of their new growth. This time, it was Mesquite Loopers, the larvae of another species of small moth.

Why did we see such enormous outbreaks of caterpillars? I had never before witnessed our mesquite trees completely stripped of their leaves by caterpillars, even though a few Mesquite Loopers are around every year. Areas near our ranch that did not see devastating hailstorms also saw much smaller outbreaks of Mesquite Loopers. What was different?

The plagues of Oak Leafrollers (which were widespread across the Hill Country) and Mesquite Loopers (which were concentrated in the areas where the hailstorms defoliated mesquite trees) are likely connected to the year's odd weather. The hard freeze in late February killed or delayed the arrival of two important foes of caterpillars—nesting birds and caterpillar parasitoids. Everyone is familiar with the former, but the latter may require some explanation.

First, the familiar—nesting birds. There was some mortality of birds from the late hard freeze, but the early April hailstorm that stripped all the vegetation from trees sent many remaining nesting birds to more productive areas. With no leaves on the trees, birds looking for nesting spots had to move on and find better places to raise their offspring.

The freeze was likely even more lethal for another caterpillar foe—tiny wasps whose larvae parasitize and eventually kill the caterpillars. Parasitoids are a type of parasite that lives in the host, but unlike most parasites, they eventually kill their hosts. This lifestyle differs from predation only in that the parasitoids keep their host alive as they grow within it, usually only killing the host as they emerge as adults. Many species of parasitoid wasps have specific hosts that they normally attack, and populations of many insects (especially moths and butterflies) are kept in check largely by their parasitoids.

The hard freeze likely killed many parasitoid wasps, as well as delaying bird nesting. This allowed Oak Leafrollers to thrive on the first leaf-out of our oaks. The April hailstorms then stripped all trees of leaves, ending that first caterpillar plague. But soon the mesquites were putting out tender new growth, which attracted the moths that produced the Mesquite Loopers. Their parasitoids had been reduced as well, and many nesting birds had moved elsewhere to raise young, so many more caterpillars survived than usual. Soon, our mesquite trees had been stripped bare for a second time.

Although the parasitoid wasps of Mesquite Loopers were much less abundant than usual, they quickly recovered with the wealth of new caterpillars to parasitize. When I collected caterpillars to send to the University of Texas Biodiversity Center for biocontrol studies, most of the caterpillars I found by day were glued to the ends of mesquite branches by their internal parasitoids. The parasitoids apparently excrete a substance, or cause their hosts to do so, that immobilizes the caterpillars on branches, to be devoured by the parasitoid larvae. I found that most of the caterpillars that managed to avoid parasitism hid by day in vegetation or debris at the base of the trees, and then climbed the trees each night to consume the tree's leaves.

By late June, most or all the caterpillars had pupated and metamorphosed into adult moths. The mesquites leafed out for a third and final time. The caterpillars provided many birds, lizards, frogs, and others animals with an abundant food source, and the adult moths then did the same for the large populations of bats in the

Hill Country. Although many people worry when we have these sudden outbreaks of caterpillars, they rarely last long and our native trees quickly recover.

I received a lot of calls and e-mails from people concerned about these "worm" (actually caterpillar) outbreaks. I advised against any kind of treatment, as caterpillars treated with pesticides are lethal to the nesting birds and other animals that feed on them. Pesticides will also kill the parasitoids that would otherwise naturally control caterpillar outbreaks, if given the chance. The short-term effects of large caterpillar outbreaks can be devastating to foliage, but if left alone, the outbreaks will not last long, and trees will quickly regenerate their lost leaves. So save your money, support local birds and other wildlife, and nature will take care of these outbreaks on its own.

41

Predators and Second Chances

Ʌ Eastern Hog-nosed Snake (*Heterodon platirhinos*), spreading its neck in Act One of its defensive drama. The swelling in its stomach is from a recently eaten toad.

Hog-nosed snakes are fascinating animals. They get their name from their up-turned snout, which is used to root for toads, their favorite prey. The coloration of hog-nosed snakes is quite variable, ranging through various shades and combinations of yellow, orange, brown, and black. The snakes usually

ʌ The same snake, moments later, in Act Two. It has now disgorged the toad and is feigning death.

have a roughly checkerboard pattern of light and dark blotches, but some individuals (especially dark ones) can be nearly uniform in coloration. The Eastern Hog-nosed Snake is fairly common in parts of the Hill Country, although like many of our native species, the population has declined in recent decades.

The thing that makes hognoses so interesting is their behavior when they are faced with a potential predator. These snakes are heavy-bodied and not very fast, so they are less able to flee than many other snakes. Instead, they try to bluff their way out of the situation. First, they do their best to look as scary and dangerous as possible. A hognose will spread its neck somewhat like a cobra does—not to mimic a cobra but to make the head look as large as possible and more like that of a viper. It inflates its main lung to increase its apparent size, and hisses loudly by releasing some of the air. At the same time, the snake will "false strike" if the potential predator gets close. It appears to be trying to bite, but it strikes with its mouth closed. Although hognoses almost never bite humans, the scary bluffing act of spread neck, loud hissing, and false striking presents a frightening picture to most people. That is why people sometimes call hog-nosed snakes "puffing adders" or "spreading adders," even though they are neither adders nor dangerous to humans. The rare reports of bites to humans have often involved the handling of captive hognoses, usually while feeding them with hands that smelled of toads. The reactions to the bites have been relatively mild pain and local temporary swelling.

If a hog-nosed snake's Act One does not work to scare away a potential threat, the snake will switch strategies. This is where things get truly comical. The snake begins to writhe around as if injured, and then opens its mouth, tongue hanging out, and rolls over on its belly to feign death. The snake will appear dead, except for one obvious clue. If you pick up the snake and turn it upright, it will immediately roll back over with its belly up and its tongue hanging out of its open mouth, like a bad actor playing dead on an old western. The snake is relying on the tendency of some birds and mammals to attack live snakes but to leave dead snakes alone. If you hide and watch, however, the snake playing dead will soon flip over and make its best effort at a quick escape.

I once found a large hognose (the one pictured here) in an area by our ranch house where I had been providing shelter for toads. When I first saw the snake, it had a large bulge in its belly, so I knew that it had eaten one of the toads. As I pulled out my camera to photograph the snake, it spread its neck, hissed at me, and started false striking. When I didn't leave, it quickly switched to Act Two of its bluff and started to writhe around as if injured, letting its mouth gape wide open and then rolling belly-up with its tongue hanging out. In doing do, it disgorged its recent meal. The disgorged toad was still quite alive, so I picked it up and washed it off. The toad quickly perked up; it seemed a little agitated but otherwise appeared largely unharmed.

The snake soon stopped playing possum and crawled off. The toad continued to hang around our house, and a few weeks after being eaten and briefly inside a snake's belly, the toad was back to its normal routines. Hog-nosed snakes have enlarged rear teeth and a venom that is thought to be effective on toads (even though it is not dangerous to humans). This hognose's venom, however, seemed to have little lasting effect on the toad, and I continued to see it regularly for the rest of the summer. It seems that we still have a lot to learn about this fascinating snake with a penchant for dramatic acting.

Bluebonnets grow around the ruins of the San Fernando Academy in Pontotoc, Texas. ➤

VII

CLIMATIC ADAPTATIONS

In 1528, Álvar Núñez Cabeza de Vaca and his men were shipwrecked on the Texas coast and enslaved by indigenous people. He and three companions eventually escaped and walked across what is now Texas and northern Mexico, moving from town to town among the native people, finally encountering Spanish settlements on the Pacific coast of Mexico in 1536. Cabeza de Vaca's stories of Texas, some exaggerated, stimulated Spanish exploration of the region.

One thing that Cabeza de Vaca did not exaggerate, however, was the speed at which weather could change in Texas. Cabeza de Vaca was impressed that

◄ Gray Treefrog (*Hyla chrysoscelis*) adaptations for arboreal life. This species has toe pads that allow it to climb trees and coloration that helps it blend into the bark and lichens on trees.

a day could start out as if it were summer, and then after the passing of a cold front, end in bitter winter. He was the first person to write about the dramatic changes in Texas weather, in the book about his adventures (*La Relación de Álvar Núñez Cabeza de Vaca*).

The plants and animals of the Hill Country are adapted to these rapid changes and sometimes harsh conditions of the Edwards Plateau. They must endure the extreme heat and drought of summer, as well as the sudden freezes that come with winter cold fronts. Different species handle summer heat and winter cold in different ways: they can leave, find ways to avoid the heat or cold, or evolve physiological mechanisms to handle the extremes. The chapters of this section explore some of the ways that plants and animals adapt to the variable weather on the Edwards Plateau.

42

Toadally Cool

⋏ A Red-spotted Toad (*Bufo punctatus*). This species is well adapted to the dry environments of the Texas Hill Country.

'll admit it: I enjoy watching toads. Given that information, you might not have been surprised to see me one hot summer day at the Double Helix as I watched a toad catch grasshoppers out in the sun. But my wife, Ann, seemed concerned when she saw me drop suddenly to my knees in the grass. She called out the only thing that she thought might get a response from me: "What is that toad doing out there in the full sun?"

Indeed, I'm sure the burning question on everyone's mind is,

"How is it that a toad could survive, and even hunt grasshoppers, out in the sun when it is 96°F in the shade?" No wonder Ann was startled and upset by my apparent sudden collapse.

The particular toad I was watching spends part of her day hunkered down in moist earth, in a spot I water around our ranch house on a nearly daily basis. But then she regularly climbs up on our porch, where she seems to enjoy sitting in the breeze on our hot summer days. She even goes out into the midday sun to forage for grasshoppers. How does she stand the heat?

Even though its skin looks dry, a toad absorbs lots of water through the granular skin of its belly, and then the water evaporates from the exposed skin. This cools the toad through a process called evaporative cooling. The theoretical limit to this cooling is the wet-bulb temperature, which can be calculated if you know the air's temperature and humidity. To get close to the wet-bulb temperature requires a constant flow of air across the body of the toad (or else the humidity will increase locally around the toad). This toad was sitting out in the breeze on a day when the air temperature was 96°F and the humidity was 27 percent. So how hot do you think the toad was?

If you guessed 72°F, I am impressed. That is very close to the wet-bulb temperature, and it was the temperature of this toad on a 96°F day. Isn't that remarkable? A toad's ability to cool itself using evaporation is quite impressive. The skin of toads is basically an efficient swamp cooler that they carry around everywhere they go.

The toads need lots of water to do this, of course, as well as relatively low humidity and a breeze. The number of places where all of those conditions exist can be relatively limited. Usually, with low humidity and a breeze, things dry out very quickly. That is why our toads like to stay around our ranch house. I spray down a patch of shady soil each day with a hose so that the toads can adsorb as much water as they need, whenever they need it. And as long as the humidity stays relatively low, and there is at least a little breeze, they can stay cool enough on our hot Texas days to go out foraging for grasshoppers even in the blazing heat and scorching sun.

Now, who is not impressed with these toads? How cool is that?

43

The Surprising Life Cycle of a Monarch Butterfly

⋏ Monarch butterfly feeding on the nectar of Blue Mistflower. *Photo courtesy of Bill J. Boyd Photography.*

E ach fall I enjoy watching the Monarchs fly south across the Double Helix Ranch, pausing to feed on Gayfeathers and Cowpen Daisies. Sometimes I even stumble across clusters of the butterflies roosting overnight in our trees. They are on a journey of 2,000 to 3,000 miles to a specific fir forest in the mountains of Michoacán, Mexico, where they have never been before.

It may seem that Monarchs are flying by at a lazy pace, but individual Monarchs have been recorded flying as much as 265 miles in a single day. Most, however, average only about 50 to 100 miles each day on their trip south. The complete trip can take as long as two months to complete.

The Monarchs that migrate through the Hill Country in the fall are the last generation of the year. They live much longer than any of the previous generations that were born in the same calendar year. These fall Monarchs are in reproductive diapause, which means that they will delay reproduction until the following February or March, as they begin the trip back to the north from the fir forests of Michoacán. Then they will mate and the females will lay tiny individual eggs on milkweed plants, which their caterpillar larvae will use as a food plant. The caterpillars sequester some toxic compounds from the milkweed that make the Monarchs distasteful to predators.

The Monarch caterpillars grow quickly on milkweed and go through five stages, called instars. The first instar caterpillars are translucent green, but the later instars are brightly marked with characteristic black, yellow, and white stripes. The fifth instar caterpillars produce a beautiful green chrysalis with gold markings, in which they will metamorphose from a caterpillar into an adult butterfly. The developing wings are folded tightly within the chrysalis, and as the adult emerges, it must pump out and unfold its wings. The total time from egg to adult is about one month.

Unlike the fall migration south, the trip north will be completed by several generations of butterflies. For each generation in the spring and summer, the adults live only about two to five weeks before they reproduce and die. Each generation flies a little farther north, eventually reaching as far as southern Canada. Then, as the summer begins to transition to fall, the migratory generation of adults is produced, and they fly south to their overwintering site in Mexico.

How do these butterflies find their way to a place they have never been? Encoded in their genes is information about how to respond to directional stimuli. Exactly how this information is encoded is not yet fully known, but the butterflies innately know which direction to fly by using several different cues. It appears that they use the magnetic field of the Earth, as well as the position of the Sun, as guides to steer south to their overwintering grounds. They must be using additional cues as they approach their winter refuge, however, as all the Monarchs from central and eastern parts of North America converge on the Oyamel Fir forest, that small, high-elevation forest where tens of thousands of butterflies may cluster on a single fir tree. The forest provides an ideal climate for the overwintering butterflies—cool and moist, but above freezing.

Until fairly recently, the overwintering Monarchs in Mexico were threatened by logging of the Oyamel Fir forest. But in 1986, Mexico created the Mariposa Monarca Biosphere Reserve to protect 62 square miles of forest for Monarch overwintering grounds. The reserve was expanded to 217 square miles of forest in 2000.

With the overwintering grounds now relatively secure, the main threat to Monarchs is found in their breeding and feeding range in northern Mexico, the United States, and southern Canada. There are several threats to the species, but one of the most pressing stems from cleaner, more efficient modern farming practices, which leave fewer milkweeds in and adjacent to agricultural land. In the spring, Monarchs rely on our native milkweeds to lay their eggs and produce the next generation of Monarchs on their trip north.

Canada, the United States, and Mexico are now working together to preserve and protect Monarch butterflies. The three countries have produced the joint North American Monarch Conservation Plan, which includes efforts to protect habitat for Monarchs in all three countries. What can you do locally? Encouraging or planting native species of milkweeds in your Hill Country garden can give Monarchs the resources they need. Some of our common native milkweeds include Antelope Horn Milkweed, Zizotes Milkweed, Green Milkweed, and Whorled Milkweed. Do not plant nonnative milkweeds from nurseries, as these plants are not available at the right time for the butterflies, and they can even disrupt normal Monarch migration patterns.

In the fall, the Monarchs migrating south need to feed on nectar, and they utilize many of our native fall-blooming flowers. One of their favorites on Hill Country ranches is the Cowpen Daisy, which seems to bloom reliably even in dry years. Other native fall flowers, such as Yellow Stonecrop, Goldenrod, and Gayfeather, are more good choices for Monarchs.

As you enjoy watching the Monarchs fly past each fall, remember to marvel at their remarkable journey and their astounding ability to fly thousands of miles to a place they have never been.

44

How Do Animals Survive the Winter?

Part 1: Migrating

ʌ White Pelicans in migration across Texas.

Although the winters on the Edwards Plateau are relatively mild by most standards, our occasional cold fronts accompanied by hard freezes often get people wondering how plants and animals survive through the winter. The species of the Hill Country use two distinct strategies. Species either leave for warmer climates, or they find a way to survive in place. I'll discuss the first strategy in this chapter and the second strategy in the next two.

Some animals survive the winter months simply by avoiding them. This is most feasible for animals that can fly long distances, including birds, bats, and some insects. Most of our local Mexican

Free-tailed Bats, including the enormous local maternal colonies in Hill Country caves, use this strategy. Most of the bats spend the winter in Mexico or Central America, where they can still find insects to eat. They leave Texas as cold fronts arrive in October or November, and they begin to return in the early spring.

More than 600 species of birds have been recorded in Texas—629 to be precise. A little over half of these (338) are Nearctic–Neotropical migratory species that breed in North America in our spring and summer and then migrate to the Neotropics (Mexico, Central and South America, or the West Indies) during the Northern Hemisphere winter. Most birds maintain high metabolic rates and body temperatures throughout the year, so they need to maximize daylight hours for foraging, living where conditions are relatively mild and food is most abundant. Hence, they move north in our summer and south in our winter. But they differ greatly in the distances they move and the places they breed and overwinter, largely depending on what they eat and the other resources that they need.

Many of the birds that breed in the Hill Country in our spring and summer spend their winters in Mexico or Central America. That is true of several of our most noticeable spring and summer breeders, including Black-chinned Hummingbirds, Painted Buntings, Scissor-tailed Flycatchers, and most of our vireos and warblers. More than 70 species of land birds migrate across the Gulf of Mexico each spring and fall between the Gulf Coast of Texas and the Yucatán Peninsula. Another 25 or so species make this migration by hugging the Gulf Coast rather than flying over open water. Others simply fly inland.

Other birds that breed in the Hill Country fly much farther south—all the way to South America—so they live in perpetual spring and summer, in two different hemispheres. Some of our common birds that make this long journey twice a year include Mississippi Kites, Common Nighthawks, Yellow-billed Cuckoos, Eastern Kingbirds, Chimney Swifts, Purple Martins, and Cliff Swallows.

Although the majority of our summer birds fly south to the Neotropics for the winter, there are also many birds that come south to Texas for the winter from the northern United States and Canada.

In the winter, we enjoy seeing many species of waterfowl on our local ponds, lakes, and rivers, such as the Gadwall, Green-winged Teal, Pintail, Mallard, and other ducks. All those species breed far to the north in the northern United States or Canada. Other common birds that we see mostly in the winter include Northern Harriers, as they glide over fields hunting for rodents; Cedar Waxwings, as they forage for winter berries; and American Goldfinches, feeding on seeds produced in the fall. Those and many more species stay in North America but shift their ranges to the warmer southern states for the winter.

As global temperatures have increased in recent years, we are beginning to see some changes in the distribution and migratory patterns of birds and other species. For example, residents of and visitors to the Hill Country have likely noticed the Black-bellied Whistling-Duck, White-winged Dove, and Crested Caracara in recent decades. Until recently, those species were found only to our south, but they have been moving farther north in recent years and are now commonly observed locally.

Not all of our local birds are migratory. Some species are here all year long. Many, such as the Bobwhite and Wild Turkey, simply shift their diets to take advantage of different food sources as the seasons change. Quail and turkeys eat a lot of fresh green sprouts in the spring and insects in the summer, and then rely mostly on seeds, including acorns, in the winter. In the case of the Bobwhite, there is usually a large population decline in the winter, followed by high rates of reproduction in the spring and summer as long as conditions are favorable. Favorable conditions include sufficient rains to produce the plants and insects that they eat, which is why quail populations often exhibit rapid changes from year to year depending on local weather conditions. Many migratory birds are less susceptible to local droughts—if the conditions are not favorable, they can move elsewhere.

The turnover in our bird, bat, and butterfly populations is part of what makes the seasonal changes fun to watch. Every year, beginning in late February, our Eastern Phoebes, Bewick's Wrens, and Eastern Bluebirds return to the Double Helix and start to nest, and soon they are busy feeding their young. By early March, we are watching with great anticipation for the first Black-chinned Hummingbird to arrive and start feeding on nectar from the spring wildflowers. When our Chimney Swifts come back each year, I marvel that such tiny birds have flown here all the way from South America. By April, we are looking for the bright plumage of our Painted Buntings.

We monitor our bird nesting boxes through the spring and summer and watch the fledglings take their first flights, marveling that they will soon be flying to a winter home they have never seen. In September, the Blue-winged Teal are our first ducks to arrive from the north, and they signal to me that fall has arrived. Soon after, the Monarch Butterflies begin to drift past on their slow flight to the mountains of Mexico. I then start to listen for the distinctive calls of Sandhill Cranes and scan the skies to find the migrating flocks. By December, the Gadwall and other ducks are on our ponds, usually after hard freezes have forced them south off the High Plains. By then, it is time for the play to begin again with the start of another year.

45

How Do Animals Survive the Winter?

Part 2: Keeping Warm and Active

Λ A Nine-banded Armadillo braving some patches of winter snow to forage for insects.
Photo courtesy of Reagan Edwards.

In the last chapter, I discussed animals that migrate to warmer places for the winter. Many other species don't leave cold weather behind, and this chapter looks at how they find ways to stay active nonetheless. (In the following chapter, I'll turn to the strategies of hibernation, brumation, and torpor—ways that animals become inactive to survive the coldest months of the year.)

Many mammals and birds remain active through the winter. They have adaptations that help protect them from winter's cold. For example, have you noticed that the coats of deer change color from winter to summer? That is because they shed their coats and grow new ones twice a year, in the fall and the spring. The reddish summer hair of deer is thin and solid, providing little insulation, which helps to prevent overheating during our warmest months. In the fall, these hairs are gradually shed and replaced by gray, thick, hollow hairs that provide excellent insulation. The hollow hairs trap air, which greatly improves their insulating ability. These hollow hairs were the inspiration for a manufactured insulation called Hollofil, which is basically a polyester version of winter deer hair. If you own a lightweight sleeping bag made from artificial fibers, it likely uses Hollofil or a similar insulation.

The other insulation that we use widely in sleeping bags and winter coats is down from ducks and geese—the fine fluffy undercoat of feathers that provides such effective insulation for waterfowl. Waterfowl produce and molt these down feathers every year, much as deer and many other mammals produce and shed a winter coat. Ducks and geese shed their down in the early summer and then grow new down feathers the following fall. Just as a down jacket is one of the warmest and lightest coats that you can buy, down provides waterfowl with the ability to stay warm even on icy winter ponds and lakes.

In addition to putting on more insulation from hair or feathers, many animals add layers of fat in the fall. This fat acts as both insulation and an energy source for producing heat through the winter. In the Hill Country, fall mast crops of fruit and nuts are especially important as food sources that animals use to add extra winter fat. In late summer, the abundant fruits of Texas Prickly Pear and Texas Persimmon are widely consumed by animals as they begin to build up winter fat reserves. Those fruits are followed by the nut crops from Pecan, Black Hickory, and especially our several species of oaks, which provide high levels of protein and fat. Birds feast on the seeds of doveweeds (*Croton* species), sunflowers, and many other fall seed crops. Without those seeds, nuts, and fruits, many animals would have a hard time building up their winter fat reserves.

Other animals stay warm in burrows or nests, protected from the cold weather, and then venture forth on warm and sunny winter days. For example, you are likely to see Nine-banded Armadillos out and about when the sun is shining and the air temperatures are not too cold in the winter, even after snow storms. As I noted in chapter 4, armadillos are a largely tropical group that originated in South America. When the Panamanian Isthmus closed a few million years ago, many groups of mammals began crossing the land bridge that had formed between North and South America. A few species of armadillos were among the northward migrants, and one species—the Nine-banded Armadillo that is now common across Texas—continues to expand northward in the United States. Although we consider armadillos to be iconic members of our local fauna, they actually moved into our area only in the late 1800s. Now, they are found far to the east and north of us, all the way to the east coast and north to southern Nebraska and Indiana.

Birds and mammals are known as endotherms, which means that they have physiological mechanisms to generate and retain heat within their bodies. In the winter, they require a lot of food to elevate their body temperatures above the cold of the season. In contrast, most other animals are ectotherms, meaning that their heat sources are largely external from their bodies. That is why you see lizards sunning on rocks and trees, or turtles sunning on logs in rivers and ponds—they are behaviorally regulating their body temperature to raise it above the ambient environmental temperature.

Many ectotherms become less active in the winter and will wait out the cold months underground or in other protected areas (see chapter 46). But some species of ectotherms are adapted to be active in our cool winters. For example, on wet winter days and nights, you are very likely to hear the loud "peep, peep, peep!" of Strecker's Chorus Frogs coming from breeding aggregations in the ponds and streams of the Hill Country. These are the first frogs to breed each year in our area, and you are likely to hear them calling beginning with the first cold rains of late fall, through the winter, and into early spring.

Although many people are familiar with the loud winter choruses of Strecker's Chorus Frogs, fewer people make the effort to find the frogs calling as they float on the water's surface or hide in vegetation around the water's edge. With a little patience and a good flashlight, you can find male Strecker's Chorus Frogs calling to the females; the males are the frogs with a large inflated vocal sac under the chin. They use the vocal sac largely to cycle air back and forth across their vocal cords, producing a remarkably loud call for such a small frog. Such choruses alert us to the best times to see these amphibian jewels, as the frogs spend most of the warmer months underground. Strecker's Chorus Frogs are members of a group that is found mostly in more northern climes, so they breed when and where it is cool and wet. They do go underground in our coldest weather, but when it is wet and above freezing, they are likely to be out in breeding choruses.

Although Strecker's Chorus Frog is an abundant and familiar species in central Texas, it was formally described and named by biologists only in 1933. Well before then, these frogs were known and studied by John K. Strecker, a famous German–American herpetologist at Baylor University. Strecker made many observations of their life history, but he thought he was observing a very different species known from central Texas, the Barking Frog. When other biologists realized that the species Strecker had studied was undescribed, they named the frog in his honor.

A walk through the winter woods and fields may reveal a lot more animal activity than you expect. If you know what to listen and look for, there is a lot of fascinating wildlife to see this time of year.

46

How Do Animals (and Plants) Survive the Winter?

Part 3: Waiting Out the Cold

⋏ A Double Helix Ranch pond after a rare winter snowstorm.

In the previous two chapters, I've discussed animals that leave for the winter and ones that remain active despite the cold. Now, I'll consider the different ways that plants and animals become dormant to survive the coldest months of the year.

Birds and mammals typically maintain relatively constant temperatures through physiological processes that generate and retain heat within their bodies, which is why they are known as endotherms. Some mammals hibernate in the cold season. During hibernation, their metabolism is depressed, their activity is greatly reduced, and their body temperature drops to near that of their surroundings. Most mammals that hibernate for the winter do so underground, where they are protected from freezing. Although the hibernation typically lasts through the winter, they may become metabolically and physically active for short periods of time. Large mammals typically store fat to last through the winter hibernation, although smaller mammals may cache stores of food that they eat during the short periods of winter activity.

Seasonal hibernation in mammals can be either obligatory (meaning that it automatically happens every winter) or facultative (meaning that it happens only if the temperatures drop or food is particularly scarce). For example, the White-tailed Prairie Dog, which lives from Montana to Colorado, where the winters are harsh, is an obligate hibernator. In contrast, our Black-tailed Prairie Dog here in Texas is a facultative hibernator—it remains active on warm winter days but may hibernate through periods of cold weather.

Most birds and many mammals do not hibernate seasonally. Instead they may use daily torpor to reduce energy expenditures on cold winter nights. The process is similar to seasonal hibernation, except that the periods of inactivity and reduced body temperature are much shorter—typically just the colder parts of a day or night. There is, however, one species of bird found in the Texas Hill Country—the Common Poorwill—that is known to hibernate seasonally. During the winter, Common Poorwills seek out shelter in piles of rocks and remain there, inactive, throughout the cold season.

Most of the reptiles (lizards, snakes, and turtles) and amphibians (frogs, toads, and salamanders) of the Hill Country are also inactive through the winter. The exceptions are largely species that live underground in caves and aquifers, where the temperature is relatively constant. Reptiles and amphibians are ectotherms, meaning that their body heat comes largely from external sources. Many species of ectotherms actively thermoregulate their body temperature, but they do so by behavioral means. They may move between sun and shade, or retreat under cover objects that are warmed by the sun, to regulate their body temperature quite precisely. During the winter, most species move underground, where their bodies are relatively cool but protected from freezing, and they remain inactive for the cold season. The term "hibernation" is also commonly applied to this period of winter inactivity by ectotherms, although some biologists prefer to restrict the term to seasonal periods of physiologically lowered metabolic activity in endotherms. When that distinction is made, the term "brumation" is used to refer to winter inactivity by ectotherms.

As our winters in central Texas are often mild, some amphibians and reptiles may be active on warm days of the winter months. Turtles are often seen sunning on rocks or logs in the winter. A few snakes are active through the winter (at least on warm days) as well. For example, I have seen Texas Patch-nosed Snakes active on the Double Helix Ranch every month of the year. These beautiful snakes, with their longitudinal black and yellow stripes, have a specialized diet that consists largely of lizards. Apparently, it is relatively easy for Texas Patch-nosed Snakes to find a winter meal of inactive lizards that are holed up for the cool season.

Although most amphibians and reptiles avoid freezing through hibernation, sometimes they may seek shelter in areas that freeze. The biggest danger with freezing is that it can rupture cells, which typically damages tissues and leads to death. Several species of amphibians and reptiles can concentrate glucose, glycogen, or other compounds in their cells to act as an antifreeze. In the winter, the water between the cells in their tissues may freeze, and the animals appear to be frozen. Nonetheless, the antifreeze compounds keep the cells from freezing, and they remain metabolically active, although at a very low rate of metabolism. For example, Gray Treefrogs can survive the freezing Hill Country winter temperatures in this way.

Many insects survive the winter using a process known as diapause. They enter a stage of delayed development in which they are typically inactive. The inactive stage is often an embryo, pupa, or larva that remains in a very low metabolic state through the winter. When warmer weather comes in the spring, dormancy is broken and development resumes. That is why some insect populations can seem to be completely absent through the winter and then suddenly appear in great numbers in the spring. Some insects also enter diapause during other seasons of the year, such as our long, hot summer months.

Plants that live in temperate climates also have to have mechanisms to survive the winter. If you have tropical house plants, you know that they are easily killed if you leave them outside in freezing weather. In contrast, our native plants survive the winter. Annual plants often do this by producing an inactive developmental stage (a seed) that can survive the winter. Many of our native perennial grasses and forbs send their energy resources into their roots for the winter, letting their stems and leaves die. Then, in the spring, the live roots send up new green growth. Other plants, such as winter-adapted cacti and other species that remain green through the winter, produce antifreeze compounds that prevent their tissues from freezing.

Deciduous trees drop their leaves in the winter largely so that they don't need to send fluids back and forth between the leaves and the roots. As the sap isn't flowing in the exposed parts of the plants during the winter, they can avoid freezing. That is why an early leaf-out of a deciduous tree is especially dangerous; a freeze late in the spring can do much more damage than the same temperatures would cause in the middle of winter, when the sap isn't flowing.

Mammiferous clouds signal heavy rain and possible violent thunderstorms. ➤

VIII

RESTORATION AND THE FUTURE OF THE HILL COUNTRY'S NATURAL RESOURCES

In recent decades, many Texas landowners have become interested in restoring the natural beauty and biodiversity of their land. They may do this for their own enjoyment and gratification, or because income from land is now often greater from recreational use than from agricultural use. Even if they use their land for agriculture, many ranchers realize that a diverse landscape of native species is often far more cost-effective and easier to maintain than is a field of planted, nonnative grasses (for example, there's no need for expensive fertilizers or herbicides). Landowners may also be aware that a biodiverse landscape takes care of itself and replenishes

< A Black-tailed Prairie Dog (*Cynomys ludovicianus*), home again in the grasslands of the Texas Hill Country.

itself in perpetuity, while maintaining the natural beauty for which the Hill Country is famous.

Hunting leases, in particular, are an important source of income for many Hill Country landowners. But with the abundant deer and other game of the Hill Country, hunting no longer presents as much of a challenge as it once did. Many hunters are now looking for a broader and deeper experience with nature while they hunt. They often wish to see a natural landscape as it might have existed before the Hill Country was settled, and to see a wide diversity of plants and animals that they are unlikely to see again once they return home.

Many Texans will remember, or have heard parents or grand-parents speak of, a past when the Hill Country's grasslands and woodlands and waterways were filled with plants and animals that are now mostly gone or greatly reduced. Big Bluestem, the Black-tailed Prairie Dog, American Beaver, Northern River Otter, American Black Bear, Texas Horned Lizard, Ornate Box Turtle, and Bobwhite are all familiar examples of species that have declined over the past century. Some of these species may be lost forever, but there is hope that we may bring back parts of the Hill Country's biodiversity to its earlier glory.

Why did these species decline? The reasons are varied. In some cases, land was overgrazed, leading to erosion and invasion of noxious, introduced plants and animals that replaced the natives. Overuse or misuse of insecticides and herbicides has contributed to declines, as has pollution from human waste disposal and other activities. Water use and diversion has made surface water less plentiful in many areas. In other cases, myths and misinformation led people to persecute certain species.

The Prairie Dog is a good example of a beneficial species that was purposefully eliminated from most of the Hill Country, largely as a result of false information and reasoning. Early ranchers saw that Prairie Dogs ate grass, so they assumed that Prairie Dogs were competing with cattle for food. They also knew that Prairie Dogs dug holes, and they reasoned that the holes might be dangerous. What if a cow stepped in a hole? Might it break its leg?

Of course, a cow has four legs, and anyone who has been around cattle knows that they don't fall down holes. Even if a cow steps in a hole with one leg, they are still standing on three legs, and they simply move the fourth leg to a more stable spot. Moreover, Prairie Dog tunnels are gently angled, so they don't present a sudden drop-off. Cows have no more trouble safely walking and grazing in Prairie Dog towns than did bison, which did so for millennia before cattle ever came to North America.

As for competition for food, Prairie Dogs do eat grass, but studies have shown that the grass that grows around a Prairie Dog town is more nutritious and desirable for cattle than grass that grows elsewhere. Prairie dog towns also stimulate and encourage a diverse array of nutritious broad-leaved plants, known as forbs. These forbs are even more nutritious and higher in protein than the grass and are thus attractive to cattle, deer, and other wildlife. Given a choice, both cattle and deer actually prefer to feed in and around a Prairie Dog town, because the grazing is actually better.

Prairie Dogs, as it turns out, are keystone species. They engineer grasslands by building their burrows and tunnels, which allow water to better penetrate the earth. The burrows themselves serve as shelters for dozens of other species of animals, such as the Burrowing Owl. Prairie Dogs are also important prey for many other species of animals. The elimination of Prairie Dogs had many unintended consequences, which led to less healthy, less diverse, less productive grasslands. As Prairie Dog towns vanished from the landscape, many other species disappeared as well.

But there is now hope for restoring Prairie Dog colonies to the Hill Country. Several private Hill Country landowners are working with Texas Parks and Wildlife staff, private groups, and biologists to bring Prairie Dogs back to their ranches. The early results have been promising; the towns are establishing but not spreading beyond the limited areas of introduction. Prairie Dogs provide entertaining nature watching, as anyone who has spent a few hours at a Prairie Dog town well knows. But they are much more important than that. Prairie Dogs are a key species that is critical to the long-term health and biodiversity of our prairies. Their return will be one step in restoring the wonderful natural beauty and stability of our country's grasslands.

On the Double Helix Ranch, I've been working to restore many of our native plants and animals, to bring the ranch back to its former biological glory and diversity. This involves reintroducing populations of various species, but before they can be brought back, the reasons for their decline must first be addressed. In most cases, that means restoration of the overall ecosystem. The following chapters discuss some of those projects and some of the challenges of restoring the native ecosystems of the Texas Hill Country, as well as issues that will need to be addressed to maintain the Hill Country's diversity and beauty into the future.

47

The Restoration and Benefits of Native Grasses

⋏ Indiangrass (*Sorghastrum nutans*) seed heads at sunrise.

W hen German settlers first came to the Texas Hill Country in the mid-1800s, they found a paradise of grasslands, with scattered oaks and other beneficial hardwoods. The grasslands were ideal for cattle, and ranches soon thrived.

Of the 324 species of grasses that have been documented from the Edwards Plateau Ecological Region, a few dozen have been introduced from elsewhere. Four of the natives dominated the original tallgrass prairies of North America: Big Bluestem, Little Bluestem, Switchgrass, and Indiangrass. All of those species still grow in

Hill Country grasslands, but they are much less abundant now than they once were. One of them—Big Bluestem—is now found only in scattered pockets of relatively undisturbed prairie. Other of our native grasses are typical of mid-grass or shortgrass prairies. The tallgrasses grow best in deeper soils, whereas thin, dry, rocky soils support much shorter grasses.

The native tallgrasses were well adapted to our cycle of flood and drought in central Texas. What you see above ground is a tiny portion of the plant. Switchgrass and Big Bluestem may grow to be six feet or more above the surface, but their roots go far deeper underground. Their deep and extensive root systems are the secret to these grasses' success. In drought, the top of the plant may die back, but the plant lives on underground. When rains eventually return, the grasses sprout new growth. The extensive root system of the native tallgrasses also helps the rain to penetrate into the soil, where it recharges our aquifers, wells, and springs. Most of our native grasses are perennial species—they are very long lived and will return year after year as long as we have appropriate rains.

Although the native grasses of the Hill Country are well adapted to our climate and provide us with many ecosystem services (such as long-term soil fertility, food and cover for both wildlife and stock, and aquifer replenishment), people often have a hard time leaving a good thing alone. Soon after settlement, ranchers began to bring in "improved" pasture grasses for hay or grazing. These exotic grasses often grow quickly if fertilized and irrigated, so they can make sense for use as a hay crop (assuming one has the resources for the large inputs of fertilizer and water necessary for them to grow well). Most of them also die out quickly if they don't get these expensive inputs.

The problem comes when the exotic grasses escape cultivation. In wet years, because they tend to grow more quickly above ground, they can shade out and displace our native grasses. Then, when the inevitable droughts come, they die out. Since the roots of the native grasses are gone, the grasses are then replaced by invasive weeds, and the grasslands are lost.

My Double Helix Ranch neighbor tells me that his grandfather

Butch Zesch was one of the Hill Country ranchers who realized the importance and benefits of our native tallgrasses in the first half of the last century. He started collecting seeds from our native tallgrasses and let them fall from a bottle on his saddle as he rode around his ranch in Mason County. Forward-thinking ranchers like Butch Zesch are a big reason why the native tallgrasses are surviving in some areas that were heavily overgrazed in the early 1900s. Today, many Hill Country ranchers understand the many benefits of native tallgrasses and are working to bring our grasslands back to their original magnificence.

Restoring native grasses is not a simple matter, however. Another reason for the resilience of our native grasses is that they have a mutualistic relationship (meaning both partners benefit) with a special kind of fungi that grows on their roots. The fungi have an enormous surface area—even bigger than the extensive roots of the plants—and they take up moisture and nutrients that are used by the plants. The plants, in turn, provide the fungi with sugars that they make through photosynthesis. Neither the grasses nor the fungi can live well without the other. When the grasses die, so do the fungi.

Unfortunately, the loss of the mutualistic soil fungi makes it very difficult to restore native grasses once they are lost. Unlike many invasive grasses, our native grasses need these fungi to thrive. So, simply sowing seeds of native grasses is often not successful, or at least not at first. It takes time for the grasses to begin to reestablish and for their mutualistic fungi to return to the soil. Many ranchers lose patience during this process and return to growing annual crops of exotic grasses. But patience, care, and effort can pay off in the long term, resulting in a healthy and productive native grass pasture that is essentially maintenance free.

Biologists are constantly studying and finding ways to reestablish native grasslands. Seeds of native grasses are now widely available commercially, and they are even grown as crops today in parts of the Hill Country. We are still learning about the details and complexities of the grasses' mutualistic fungi and how they can be restored in places where they have been lost. One trick that seems to help is to transplant a few whole plants of native grasses into fields that have been sown with their seeds. The fungi on the transplanted grasses can help the seedlings get established and thrive.

With hard work and perseverance, we may see the grasslands of the Hill Country restored to their former glory. These grasslands can be beneficial to everyone. Ranchers can enjoy profitable, low-maintenance range; native wildlife that has nearly disappeared with the loss of the grasslands can return and flourish; and everyone can appreciate the natural beauty and services provided by our native prairie.

48

The Pros and Cons of Brush Control

⋏ Fragrant Mimosa (*Mimosa borealis*, foreground), a shrub often removed by landowners as unwanted brush. Patches of this plant provide important cover for many species, including Bobwhite.

I regularly meet with other Hill Country ranch owners to discuss their management efforts and their interest in increasing wildlife populations and biodiversity on their property. As I rode around one day with a relatively new ranch owner, he showed me various plants that he planned to manage or eliminate and asked me what I thought about them. Before answering that type of question, I always start by asking the landowners what goals they hope to achieve. Are you interested only in raising livestock? Are you interested in wildlife populations, such as deer and quail? Do you have an interest in restoring the land and increasing overall biodiversity of plants and animals?

Many new landowners, in particular, seem to have an idealized view of grasslands as pure stands of grass, much like a lawn of a suburban home. In reality, however, healthy, native grasslands do not resemble that picture at all. A healthy, productive, diverse grassland includes a wide variety of broad-leaved plants called forbs, as well as clumps of woody, often thorny, vegetation. The forbs are especially important food for most species of wildlife, as well as for livestock. White-tailed Deer, for example, eat very little grass. They eat only the tender green shoots of newly sprouted grasses and cannot digest mature grass efficiently. White-tailed Deer would starve if confined to a field of nothing but mature grass.

Deer change their diet throughout the year. In the spring, they mostly consume tender green forbs. By late summer, most of the forbs are dried up, and the deer switch to eating a lot of mast— the fruits of plants like Prickly Pear Cactus and Texas Persimmon. They also begin to rely more on browsing the leaves of trees and other woody vegetation. The green forbs return with fall rains, and then (in most years) our abundant oaks produce acorns, another important mast crop. Through the winter, deer will continue to eat forbs, browse on trees, and search for the last of the acorns from the fall. Then spring brings another flush of green growth, and the cycle repeats.

If landowners choose to eliminate all vegetation except grass, then they are creating a field where cattle and some other livestock can survive, but relatively few other animals will thrive. Even cattle need the added protein that comes from forbs, unless they receive a purchased protein supplement. In addition to the food value of forbs and woody vegetation, many species of animals need brush, rock piles, and thorny vegetation for cover.

As the new ranch owner took me on a tour of his property, he stopped at an isolated Lotebush (*Ziziphus obtusifolia*) in one of his pastures. "Whatever this is, I'm going to eliminate it," he said. "Why?" I asked. "Because it is thorny." I already knew from our conversation that he was interested in seeing quail numbers improve, so I explained that some scattered clumps of thorny Lotebush were exactly what he needed for quail. Quail seek out Lotebush because it is so spiny; those spines keep predators from attacking quail as they rest. Remove the Lotebush, and the quail would have no place to hide from hawks and other predators. As we drove around and looked at other native vegetation, he seemed surprised to learn that much of what we identified and discussed had beneficial qualities that might not seem obvious at first glance.

In addition to providing effective wildlife cover, Lotebush also produces small black fruits that are relished by both quail and deer. Lotebush is in the same genus as the Jujube, or Chinese Date of Asia (*Ziziphus jujuba*). Although the fruits of North American *Ziziphus* are not as widely relished by humans as are those of the Asian species, native North Americans ate the fruit and used it to make a drink and several medications. Furthermore, a Lotebush in fruit is quite attractive. In most circumstances, Lotebush is a highly desirable species for the range that benefits many species of wildlife.

Some native species of brushy plants can indeed be invasive in pastures, of course. In parts of the Hill Country where limestone rocks dominate, Ashe Juniper (commonly called cedar) can become troublesome. This tree was originally controlled by regular wildfires, but when fires are suppressed, it can become very dense and crowd out almost everything else. Although scattered clumps of juniper can provide good cover, if prescribed burns are not used, then juniper likely will need to be cut and thinned in some areas.

Juniper is not a problem on the Llano Uplift. It grows poorly in the sandy, acidic sands formed from weathered granite and gneiss that underlie most of our landscape. In those areas, it is Honey Mesquite that can become invasive, especially on range that has been overgrazed by livestock. Mesquite has many beneficial qualities, including its ability to fix nitrogen in the soil, a characteristic of legumes (members of the bean family). Our sandy soils tend to be deficient in nitrogen, so mesquites are important for maintaining soil fertility. Certainly, there can be too much of a good thing. A few scattered mature mesquites are beneficial, but a thicket of emerging mesquite seedlings will crowd out everything else and can make a pasture nearly impassable.

As noted in chapter 26, mesquite seeds have to pass through the digestive system of a mammal before they will germinate. When cattle or other livestock eat mesquite beans, the animals pass the seeds around the pasture, and then help plant the seeds as they disturb the soil with their hooves. Where cattle are concentrated for long periods of time, mesquite seedlings can appear everywhere and become problematically dense. The solution is to avoid over-grazing a pasture. Cattle rarely eat mesquite beans unless there is little other choice. With appropriate stocking rates and rotational grazing, invasive mesquite problems should not arise in the first place.

Prickly Pear Cactus and Texas Persimmon are two other brush species that many landowners wish to control. Like mesquite, they tend to become invasive in overgrazed pastures. But these plants have many positive qualities, as long as they don't become the dominant cover. If you go walking through a Hill Country landscape on a hot, dry August day, what do you find that deer and other wildlife might be using for food? The leaves of trees are still green, and deer will browse on those. The other important foods of late summer, however, are mast crops. In most of the Hill Country, many tons of ripe Prickly Pear fruits (tunas) and fruits of Texas Persimmons are important for deer in the late summer, especially after most of the vegetation has burned to a crisp. Without these mast crops, we could not sustain the deer populations for which the Hill Country is justifiably famous. Clumps of Prickly Pear also provide important cover for a wide diversity of small animal species.

After driving around with the new ranch owner all morning, I sensed that he began to have a new appreciation for plant diversity and its importance. Sometimes, the best management practice is to accept and embrace the diversity of the land and its vegetation, and to recognize that many native plants have important beneficial qualities that contribute to a healthy range. That approach gives us more time to control the spread of introduced invasive species, many of which do require active management strategies.

49

Recovery of a Texas Icon

The Texas Horned Lizard

ʎ A pair of Texas Horned Lizards (*Phrynosoma cornutum*), working for recovery.

Many Texas residents born in the 1960s or earlier have fond memories of playing with abundant Texas Horned Lizards in their yards or in open areas around their hometown. These lizards were usually called horny toads or horned frogs, although they are lizards rather than amphibians. Their slow gait, easy-going personalities, and delightful appearance (to many, they look like miniature dinosaurs) delighted children of all ages. Some children would take them to school, where (if they had tolerant teachers) they would carry the lizard around on their clothing or in a pocket.

A lucky few would get to see the lizard's surprising defensive display. If startled by a potential predator, a Horned Lizard can eject a stream of blood from its eye. It does this primarily in response to canids (dogs, foxes, and coyotes, for example). The blood is highly irritating and distasteful to canids, and they will quickly drop and abandon a Horned Lizard if it uses this defense. Sometimes, even a human will elicit this response from a threatened Horned Lizard. I was once photographing a Horned Lizard when it squirted me, and I can confirm that the blood stings when it gets in one's eye. But humans very rarely get close enough to a Horned Lizard to get hit in the face by the blood stream, and the vast majority of Horned Lizards are calm and harmless enough for even small children to handle.

What makes Horned Lizard blood so distasteful to canids? The answer to that question is not yet clear. It is thought that the lizards are probably sequestering distasteful compounds from their primary prey, Harvester Ants. Horned Lizards eat a variety of small insects, but the bulk of their diet is made up of a few species of ants and termites. In particular, large red Harvester Ants are the primary food item of Horned Lizards in central Texas.

Horned Lizards rapidly declined in eastern and central Texas beginning in the 1970s, and they have completely disappeared from many areas where they used to be abundant. A generation of Hill Country residents have grown up without the delight of knowing Horned Lizards. What caused this decline? It appears that a number of factors were involved. The spread of imported fire ants and the correlated decline of Harvester Ants was a major factor. Fire ants are not tolerant of other ants, and they can overwhelm most of our native ants with their high population numbers. In addition, the imported fire ants attack and eat the eggs of many ground-nesting species, including the eggs of Horned Lizards. As the imported ants moved across Texas, many landowners tried to use ant poisons to stop their spread. Unfortunately, the poisons were often broadcast over large areas, and they were much more effective at killing Harvester Ants and other native species than they were at stopping the spread of fire ants. General insecticide use also contributed to the decline of the Horned Lizards' favorite food items. Fortunately, biologists have now introduced a tiny fly that parasitizes fire ants, and they are a significantly smaller problem than they were when they first came to the Hill Country. On well-managed ranches, Harvester Ants are beginning to recover.

Even as Horned Lizard prey declined in the latter part of the 1900s, populations of Horned Lizard predators rapidly increased. Lizards are eaten by a wide variety of birds and mammals, but raccoons are especially effective Horned Lizard predators. Raccoons eat Horned Lizard eggs, hatchlings, and adults. Populations of raccoons have exploded since the 1970s, partly because of supplemental feeding by humans (with food intended for deer), and partly because of a crash in the market for raccoon pelts. So, we humans created ideal conditions for Horned Lizard predators and at the same time greatly reduced Horned Lizard prey.

Today, Texas Horned Lizards can still be found in western portions of the Hill Country, but they have been eliminated from the eastern and central parts of the region. Even where they persist, the remaining populations in the Hill Country are barely hanging on. There is hope, however, for their recovery. On ranches that still have remnant populations, management practices that encourage native Harvester Ants and control raccoon populations are showing promising increases in Horned Lizard populations. Perhaps as the populations recover, they will begin to spread to other areas.

In addition, several Texas zoos (including those in Fort Worth and San Antonio) have developed Horned Lizard head-start programs. At those institutions, Horned Lizards are bred in captivity and the young are released back into the wild. One site where reintroductions have occurred is at Mason Mountain Wildlife Management Area. It appears that these reintroductions have been successful, as some of the young Horned Lizards have overwintered and continue to grow in their new homes.

With work from biologists, zoos, and cooperating landowners, we may see Horned Lizards return one day as the delightful and welcome Texas icon that older residents remember with such fondness from their youth.

50

Avoiding the Dangers of Lead Poisoning in Game Meat

⋀ Crested Caracaras fighting over a coyote carcass. Animals shot with lead ammunition can poison scavengers such as caracaras. *Photo by Melody Lytle.*

Lead poisoning results in more than half a million human deaths worldwide every year. Far more people than that are harmed by lead poisoning. Our brains and nervous systems are especially sensitive to lead. Lead poisoning is strongly associated with a wide range of neurological problems, including lowered IQ, increased rates of attention deficit hyperactivity disorder, memory problems, sleep disorders, depression, and hearing loss. It is one of the most common environmental causes of decreased intellectual ability and behavioral problems in children. Lead poisoning can also result in kidney failure, cardiovascular disease, muscular problems, and loss of reproductive functions, among a host of other serious problems.

We are all exposed to lead in our environment, in the food we eat, and in the water we drink. Where does the lead come from? Almost all of the lead we are exposed to comes from human activities and uses. Humans mine lead and use it for a multitude of purposes. It ends up in our houses, in our food, and in our water supply. When the dangers of lead poisoning became clear in the 1970s, the United States began to introduce policies to reduce or eliminate lead in paint and gasoline, which dramatically lowered environmental lead and lead poisoning levels in many people. Some people, however, are still exposed to high levels of lead in their diet and water.

The problems of lead poisoning are not limited to humans. Lead is a serious toxin for most species of plants and animals. Birds are especially sensitive to lead poisoning, and many birds ingest lead fragments left in their environment by humans. Lead shot is especially a problem for waterbirds, and lead bullet fragments are commonly ingested by scavengers. Lead ammunition and lead from fishing weights also ends up in our waterways, where it increases lead concentrations in water. Lead concentrations in fish are now so high in many areas that fish consumption must be restricted out of concern for safety.

Many sources of lead poisoning can easily be eliminated. Alternatives to lead are available for most uses, just as we have found alternatives to lead in paint and gasoline. For Hill Country residents and hunters, one of the major sources of lead poisoning is the lead in bullet fragments in game meat. Lead is a very soft metal, and it liquefies when bullets hit a target at high speeds. The tiny droplets of lead spread through nearby tissues and contaminate the surrounding meat. If that lead ends up in your diet, it will raise the lead concentration in your blood. Any increase in lead concentration is considered unhealthy.

Fortunately, there are simple, safe, and effective alternatives to lead ammunition. All waterfowl hunting now requires nontoxic shotgun loads, which protect both wildlife and humans from lead poisoning. In Texas, however, most rifle hunters still use lead bullets for deer, hogs, and other large game. Nonetheless, copper and copper-alloy bullets (such as gilding metal, which is a copper-zinc alloy) are now widely available. They are marked on the box as nontoxic. Copper and gilding metal bullets were originally developed because they are more effective than lead for large game. Unlike lead bullets, they open into a perfect mushroom shape and retain virtually 100 percent of their weight on impact. They do not fragment like lead bullets, and they are not toxic. Since they hold together and open effectively, they produce quick, efficient, and humane kills of game animals.

Years ago I began requiring nontoxic bullets for all hunters on the Double Helix Ranch. Nontoxic ammunition is now available for virtually all calibers of hunting arms. I've found solid gilding metal rifle bullets to be more effective than lead bullets, and just as accurate. All of the hunters at my ranch have reported the same. I take satisfaction in knowing that the meat from the game animals we take is not contaminated with lead. I also rest easier knowing that the carcasses and remains from gutting game animals are not poisoning wildlife on my ranch and are not contaminating my soil and water with lead.

Some states and wildlife refuges now require all hunters to use nontoxic ammunition. In Texas, with the exception of waterfowl hunting, it is still a choice that is left up to hunters. So why wouldn't hunters choose to use nontoxic ammunition when hunting game? I have heard people give several explanations, none of which seem compelling. Probably the biggest reason is that nontoxic ammunition is less available; it isn't sold in many smaller, local stores, whereas lead ammunition is ubiquitous. This is a chicken-and-egg problem. People don't use nontoxic ammunition because it isn't easily available, and it isn't easily available because most people don't use it yet. This issue will change once more people understand the dangers of lead ammunition and begin to demand nontoxic loads. Until then, nontoxic loads are carried by larger hunting supply stores and are easily available for purchase online. Availability of nontoxic loads has never been a problem for any of the hunters on my ranch.

A second issue that is commonly mentioned is price; copper or gilding metal bullets are more expensive than lead bullets. However, the price of nontoxic bullets is similar to premium lead ammunition, and any difference in the cost of ammunition for a season of hunting is a tiny percentage of the overall cost of hunting. It is a very small price to pay to avoid the serious consequences of lead contamination.

The third reason I've heard is based largely on misinformation. Some people claim that nontoxic loads lead to greater copper-fouling of rifle barrels. Modern lead rifle bullets, however, are jacketed in gilding metal, so the outside of the bullets (the part that contacts the rifle barrel) is identical to solid gilding metal bullets. Pure copper bullets are somewhat softer, so I choose gilding metal bullets (such as the Hornady GMX); fouling from these bullets does not differ from standard jacketed lead bullets and in any case is easily cleaned from barrels with appropriate solvents.

I've heard some people claim that nontoxic bullets are less accurate than lead bullets. That has not been my experience. I think this likely comes from people who try nontoxic bullets only once. Many guns work best with certain styles or loads of bullets, whether they are lead or nontoxic options. A little experimentation is often required to find the most accurate loads for any gun, whether one uses lead or nontoxic rounds.

The biggest obstacles to change seem to be tradition and inertia. People who have been hunting all their lives don't like to make changes in their gear without a good reason. I agree; neither do I. But I see the problem of lead poisoning as a serious issue—one that is easily addressed with a small change that requires little cost or effort. In Texas, it is a choice. But isn't it the responsible thing to do—for your health, for the health of your friends and family, and for the health of the world around us?

51

Our Climate Future in Central Texas

⋏ Preparing for an approaching wildfire on the Double Helix Ranch. With global climate change, wildfires are expected to become more frequent. *Photo by Amy Zesch.*

When people think about the future of the Hill Country, the topic of global climate change often comes up. Is it real? How serious is it? When will it affect central Texas? How will it affect the ecosystems of the Edwards Plateau? Is there anything we can do about it?

Let's begin with the fact of global climate change. There is no doubt that the Earth is warming rapidly at present. We set new records for global heat almost every year now. The increase may seem slow in terms of a human lifetime, but the rate of temperature increase is unprecedented in geological terms. Yes, in the distant past the Earth has been warmer than it is now. About 50 million years ago, in the Eocene epoch, carbon dioxide levels in the atmosphere were far greater than they are today, probably because of an extended period of massive volcanic eruptions. Carbon dioxide acts like a greenhouse cover for the Earth, trapping the heat from sunlight close to the Earth's surface. As a result, the Earth was about 14°F (8°C) warmer, on average, in the Eocene than it is today. There was no polar ice, the ocean levels were much higher, and the climate of Texas (and everywhere else) was completely different. For example, in the Eocene, the Chisos Mountains in west Texas were covered in tropical rain forests, and little primates called tarsiers lived in trees on the slopes of the mountains. That is hard to imagine if you visit the dry desert mountains in Big Bend National Park today.

If the Earth's climate has changed before, long before humans had anything to do with the change, why are we so concerned now? Previous changes to the climate typically happened gradually, over many millions of years. In contrast, we are now seeing rapid temperature changes over just a few decades—thousands to hundreds of thousands of times faster than most earlier climatic shifts.

Populations of plants and animals can adapt to change and move their ranges over the course of thousands to millions of years. But many species cannot adapt and change fast enough to deal with the rapid climate change that we are now experiencing. Moreover, some of the results of such major climatic change would devastate the world's human populations and economies. For example, major coastal cities like Houston would be under water from rising sea levels. The displacement of many millions of people from coastal cities would make our current immigration issues seem trivial by comparison. Refugee crises and changes to our agricultural systems would be massive.

Why is the climate changing so quickly? The ultimate reason is the same as it was in the Eocene, namely, increasing carbon dioxide (and some other gases, such as methane) in our atmosphere. The difference this time is that humans are producing most of this carbon dioxide. We are extracting fossil remains of organisms (oil, gas, and coal) that were deposited over the course of many millions of years and burning them. That releases carbon dioxide and other gases into our atmosphere, which results in rapid changes to the climate.

Why is it such a big deal if the average global temperature increases several degrees in our lifetimes? Aren't we used to dealing with heat in Texas? Unfortunately, the increase in temperature drives many other changes. Polar glaciers melt, the water flows into the oceans, and the level of the oceans rises. The changes in temperature cause massive changes in the rainfall patterns. Average global rainfall actually increases with global warming, but so does evaporation. Some areas of the Earth will get much wetter than they are today, as the Big Bend region did in the Eocene. But many other areas will get much drier. In general, the western United States is predicted to get much drier with current global warming, and we are already seeing increasing droughts and increasing wildfires in this region.

Model predictions for the future climate of central Texas are not all in agreement. Many models show increasing variability in our future climate, with increasing periods of droughts punctuated by significant floods. There are indications that we are already seeing the beginning of these changes today, as evidenced by our many record droughts and floods of recent years. Predictions of how these changes will affect future life in the Hill Country are somewhat speculative, but one thing is clear: many of those changes will have major economic, biological, and social consequences in the coming decades.

Is there anything we can do to slow the change? Yes, there are many options available to us, and many are beneficial to humans in multiple ways. The biggest issue is finding alternative sources of energy that reduce our reliance on fossil fuels. Fortunately for us, Texas has excellent opportunities for solar power development. For example, we converted our Double Helix Ranch to solar power many years ago, and ever since then, we have produced more electricity than we have consumed. Our local electric cooperative buys back the excess power that we produce at the same wholesale rate that it pays to buy power elsewhere, so even people without solar power systems are already using some excess solar power produced by others.

At our ranch, we run our houses, our cars, and even our all-terrain vehicles on solar-produced electricity, and we still feed excess electricity back into the grid. The solar panels are on rooftops, so they take up no land. Electric cars are far more powerful and less expensive to run in the long term; they are also a pleasure to drive. The solar rooftop system has an expected lifetime of several decades, and its initial cost will soon be covered by all our savings on electricity. After that, the solar system makes us money every year, contributing in a positive way to our bottom line.

There is no reason that the Texas Hill Country could not become a net energy-producing area through solar power. The main obstacle for many is the initial cost of solar energy systems. They more than pay for themselves in time, but the initial investment is prohibitive to some. Our forward-thinking, local Habitat for Humanity Program builds solar-equipped and energy-efficient houses for those in need of affordable housing. We need more solutions like that. Private and public investment in solar power (as well as other renewable sources of energy, especially wind) is our best hope for reducing the devastating effects of climate change, while benefiting everyone with cleaner air, cleaner water, and a more prosperous economy.

52

If the Earth Is Warming, Why Did We Have a Record Cold Snap?

⋏ Oak trees in the snow during a record cold snap in 2021.

Why do we continue to set record cold temperatures in the Hill Country, given that the average temperature of the Earth is increasing as a result of increasing levels of greenhouse gases in our atmosphere?

To understand unusual cold spells, it is first important to understand the difference between weather and climate. "Weather" refers to the specific conditions that we experience on a given day at a particular place and time: the temperature, humidity, rainfall, snowfall, wind speed, cloud cover, etc. Climate, in contrast, refers to the long-term averages of those conditions for a specified area and season. Climate is based on long-term seasonal averages, whereas weather refers to the specific conditions we experience each day. From years of record-keeping, we know that the average high temperature for February in Mason, Texas, is 65°F (18°C), and the average low for the month is 36°F (2°C). That is information about the climate of the area around Mason. But knowledge of the average doesn't tell you what you can expect on any given February day, when it might be sunny and 90°F or snowing and 10°F. Nonetheless, knowledge of our climate lets you know that any given day in February in Mason is likely to be cooler than any given day in August, when it is very likely to be hot. In contrast to summer, when it is hot almost every day, our weather in winter months is much more variable, from very cold and icy to warm and sunny.

We also have lots of long-term data that relate various physical measurements to the average climatic conditions. We know, for example, that the Earth's average temperature increases as a function of atmospheric carbon dioxide concentration. As atmospheric carbon dioxide increases, it traps heat at the Earth's surface, and the average temperature of the Earth increases. The carbon dioxide functions much like the glass on a greenhouse. We call this phenomenon global climate warming, because the increase in atmospheric greenhouse gases results in an increase in the average temperature of the Earth's surface.

The documented average temperature of the Earth has increased a couple of degrees (Fahrenheit) over the past few decades, and it is expected to continue increasing as long as we continue to produce and release more greenhouse gases into the atmosphere. That increase in atmospheric carbon dioxide has resulted in an increase in the number of our summer days that exceed 100°F (38°C) each summer, which is why we have experienced a series of record hot summers in central Texas. We will likely continue to break records for high temperatures in the coming decades, as average global warming increases.

It may seem counterintuitive, then, that an increase in average global temperatures can also result in major cold-weather events, like some of those we have seen in recent winters. The increase in average global temperature is not equally distributed across the planet, and the polar regions of the Earth are warming especially quickly. This is unfortunate for several reasons. First, increased temperatures at the poles cause melt-off of global ice caps. Polar ice on land melts and drains into the oceans, which raises sea levels. That is not a direct danger to central Texas, which is far above sea level, but it will result in increasing flooding of coastal areas around the world over the coming century. Since most of the largest cities of the world are in coastal regions, this will have an enormous effect on human population movements in coming decades.

A second major effect of rapidly warming polar regions is the destabilization of the Polar Vortex. A polar vortex is a current of high wind that normally encircles each pole of the Earth. In North America, we are particularly interested in the Northern Polar Vortex, which normally keeps frigid polar air trapped far to our north. Unfortunately, with global warming, the Polar Vortex becomes destabilized, and the winds that encircle the North Pole begin to wobble. The Northern Polar Vortex then develops dips that extend far south of normal, and very cold polar air moves into areas where it would not normally occur. When that happens, air that would normally be kept close to the North Pole can move south all the way into Texas and northern Mexico. The result is record cold weather for our area, and all the problems that it causes. Because an increase in average global temperature can result in local weather events that are both hotter and colder than normal, it makes sense to refer to the changes that are occurring as "global climate change." Average global warming will indeed result in increased weather variability, including hotter highs and colder lows for the Hill Country.

The other major effects that we can expect from average global warming are changes in local evaporation and rainfall. As the Earth's average temperature increases, more water evaporates into the atmosphere. But what goes up must come down, so increases in evaporation result in increased precipitation, as the two have to equalize over time. This is known as the water cycle. The atmosphere can only hold so much water before it begins to precipitate out as rain. This may sound like good news for drought-prone regions like the Hill Country, but unfortunately, the increased evaporation and increased precipitation will not necessarily occur in the same areas. Thus, another major effect of global climate change is that some areas of the Earth will see increasing likelihood of droughts, and other areas will have an increasing likelihood of floods. Much of the western United States, for example, is expected to see increasing droughts this century, whereas some regions in the eastern and northern United States may see increased rainfall. Rainfall in Texas is likely to become more variable, with increases in both droughts and floods. We are already beginning to see this effect. Over the past few decades we have set records for both droughts and floods. Consider the one-year drought of record in 2011, for example, and recall the record flooding of Hill Country rivers in recent years.

Global climate change means increased variability in our local weather. We can expect hotter summer spells, as well as colder winter spells, as well as stronger major storm events. We will likely continue to set new records for droughts and floods. The economic, biological, cultural, and social effects of these changes in central Texas are expected to be severe.

What, if anything, can we do about our changing climate? Our actions as individuals may seem insignificant, and in a way that is true. The changes we are discussing are the result of the collective actions of billions of people who inhabit our planet. Only massive societal change might reverse the course of global climate change. But if individuals, local communities, states, nations, and people everywhere make changes, we can reduce the production of greenhouse gases and slow or possibly even stop human-induced climate change. By far the largest and most practical changes we can make are in how we produce our electricity and in transportation. We can make improvements in other areas as well, but unless we reduce carbon dioxide production from energy generation and transportation, there is little hope of making significant progress in slowing climate change. We have only a short window of time in which we can make these vital decisions that will have an enormous impact on our children's and grandchildren's generations.

53

Practical, Painless, and Significant Solutions to Climate Change

⅄ Double Helix Ranch headquarters, including the solar arrays on outbuildings that power the ranch.

I n this chapter, I will not attempt to convince anyone that global climate change is happening. If you haven't noticed climate change for yourself by now, then no amount of new information is likely to change your mind. Suffice it to say that the fact of global climate change is clear and extraordinarily well documented.

I'm also not going to place blame on anyone or any group for the climate change crisis. Increases in atmospheric carbon dioxide are the largest physical factor in our changing global climate. Humans contribute to those increases in many different ways, and all of us are at least partly responsible. As we all contribute to the problem, I'll assume that any responsible person will want to be a part of the solution as well. Besides, we all live here and presumably care about our planet.

You may have heard people say or imply that the climate change problem is hopeless, and there is nothing that we can do to save the Earth, or that the changes that will be needed to do so are so great that we simply cannot afford to attempt them. None of that is true. This chapter is about some relatively simple changes you can make in your life that will not only help address the climate change problem but will also improve your quality of life at the same time.

There are hundreds of practical ways to reduce carbon emissions, as well as ways to sequester carbon from the atmosphere. If you are interested in more detail, I recommend looking at the suggestions listed at Project Drawdown, which you can explore at https://www.drawdown.org/solutions/table-of-solutions. Project Drawdown estimates that it will require a reduction or sequestering of approximately 1,000 gigatons of carbon over the next three decades to hold global temperature increases to 2°C (3.6°F) by the end of this century, and a reduction of about 1,500 gigatons to hold temperature increases to 1.5°C (2.7°F). Project Drawdown lists a set of practical solutions that can produce those reductions.

Project Drawdown presents ambitious but completely achievable goals, and meeting those goals will mean the survival and protection of the Earth for our children and grandchildren. How do we get there? It will take a combination of many solutions, but some solutions have a much greater impact than others. Let's look at solutions that have the biggest impact and the greatest upside and discuss what they will require.

In the Project Drawdown scenario that holds global temperature increases to 1.5°C, by far the biggest savings come from changes in how we generate electricity. Developing solar power can account for a reduction of 226 gigatons in atmospheric carbon over the next 30 years. Wind energy generation can give us another 160-gigaton reduction. Although some centralized power projects involving wind and solar are needed, adding solar power to your home can save you considerable money while you help reduce carbon emissions.

Adding solar power to your house or ranch requires a substantial initial investment, but if you can afford it, it has a virtually guaranteed return. It takes about 8 years for the average solar energy installation to pay for itself. Solar panels have an expected lifetime of at least 25 years, and likely much longer. After they have paid for themselves, solar panels are expected to provide you with decades of free and reliable energy. Who wouldn't love that?

The next biggest category of carbon reduction solutions, after electricity generation, relates to changes in agriculture and food use. The most important single change we can make in this area is simply reducing food waste. Reducing food waste could save us more than 100 gigatons of carbon in three decades. We will still need to produce food, but if we waste less we can produce less. Not wasting food also means saving money and reducing world hunger.

All food production is carbon intensive, but how we produce it matters a great deal. Changing our agricultural practices can result in more big savings. For example, one big area of potential savings comes from silvopasture cattle ranching. That is a big name for a method of cattle production that is already widely used in parts of the Hill Country, including on our Double Helix Ranch. It simply means the integration of cattle, trees, and grass forage on natural rangelands that are largely unsuitable for other types of agriculture. Natural cattle pastures with trees can sequester 5 to 10 times as much carbon as do treeless pastures, and cattle can be raised without growing grain to convert to meat (which is wasteful and carbon intensive). Retaining or replanting scattered native trees in natural rangelands, combined with appropriate range management, helps sequester carbon in soils and protects natural rangeland, all while efficiently producing food for human populations. If you don't raise cattle yourself, you can help by buying range-fed beef rather than grain-fed beef. Reducing the amount of meat in our diet would help as well, particularly by allowing a transition to more sustainable practices of animal production.

If you don't want to reduce your meat intake or switch to range-fed beef, you can still help by eating the Hill Country's abundant feral hogs. There is no environmental downside to harvesting and consuming feral hogs. Feral hogs are major contributors to atmospheric carbon, both through their consumption of plants and animals and their constant disturbance of topsoil. The more feral hogs you eat, the less other food you will eat, and you will help control a highly problematic and damaging introduced species. Pork from feral hogs is in great demand in parts of Europe and Asia, and now some high-end restaurants in Austin (such as Dai Due) specialize in feral hog delicacies.

The third major area where we can make significant, painless changes is transportation. Increasing public transportation opportunities in cities results in big carbon savings. People need transportation between cities as well, and high-speed electric trains are a comfortable, convenient, economic, and efficient solution. Much transportation (across the Hill Country, certainly) will still require personal vehicles, but changing from internal combustion engines to electric cars and trucks can reduce carbon emissions considerably. The good news is that electric vehicles (EVs) are also faster, safer, quieter, more reliable, and less expensive to own and operate over their lifetime. If you haven't yet driven an EV, you will be pleasantly surprised by the experience when you do. It won't be long—by about 2035, most new vehicles will be EVs.

This planet is worth saving, and the changes noted above require little or no sacrifice on our part. Most of these steps make the world a safer and better place to live, while they also help save the world from environmental disaster. By implementing these solutions, we have everything to gain, and nothing to lose. Isn't it past time to act?

54

Six Resolutions for Supporting
Native Plants and Animals

⋏ A Texas Nature Conservancy preserve at the western edge of the Hill Country. The
focus here is restoring native plants and animals.

I'm often asked what individuals can do to help restore and conserve the natural beauty and biodiversity of the Texas Hill Country. Even a small yard or garden provides opportunities for positive action. Ranch owners may wish to take on larger projects. Anyone can volunteer for projects and workdays with conservation and wildlife organizations. Here are a half-dozen simple ideas for projects you might consider if the natural beauty and diversity of the Texas Hill Country is something that you treasure and wish to help restore and protect.

1. Preserve, protect, and restore riparian areas and wetlands. Our stunningly beautiful spring-fed rivers of the Hill Country are a focal point for recreation. Swimmers, canoers, kayakers, anglers, birdwatchers, geology enthusiasts, and nature lovers all enjoy the Llano, Pedernales, Colorado, Guadalupe, Medina, Frio, Nueces, Devils, and Pecos Rivers. These waterways are also critical habitat for many of the Hill Country's aquatic plants and animals, and their vegetated valleys provide habitat for many other species. The primary threats to these waterways are pollution and degradation from human activities, including sedimentation from erosion of surrounding rangelands. Invasion of nonnative plants along the rivers is also a serious threat in places.

Residents and visitors to the Hill Country should be especially concerned with properly and safely disposing of waste and hazardous materials. Nothing should be thrown or allowed to run into rivers, creeks, or wetlands. Landowners should protect riparian corridors from overgrazing and allow a vegetative buffer that will greatly reduce erosion. Building catchment ponds in pastures also reduces erosion, captures soil, and provides local water resources for many species of animals. Seasonal ponds that do not support predatory fishes are especially important as breeding sites for amphibians, which have declined alarmingly in the Hill Country in recent decades.

2. Restore a pocket prairie. The Hill Country is well known for its stunning displays of spring wildflowers. Have you noticed, however, that many of the best displays are often found along the right-of-way of a public road? Many pastures are too heavily grazed to support healthy, diverse populations of native grasses and wildflowers. Nonnative grasses and other invasive plants quickly move into such pastures and displace the natives. That reduces the seed production from the native species, which makes it harder for them to return even once the overgrazing ends. The native grasses and wildflowers are not only beautiful but also provide important food and shelter for much of our native wildlife.

Restoring the native prairie plants in open grassland areas requires patience and effort. Many people get frustrated trying to restore large areas all at once. Consider picking a small area to restore—perhaps even an area around your house. Native plant seeds are grown and marketed locally (for example, by Native American Seed in Junction). Restoring a small pocket prairie will provide a seed source from which the prairie can slowly expand and recover, and it will provide important host plants for native animals. The companies that provide native seeds for this purpose also provide advice and books on restoration projects. After you learn what works best for your small site, you can encourage its expansion.

3. Remove invasive trees and replace them with natives. Unfortunately, several invasive, nonnative trees have been marketed as landscape trees in the Hill Country. These invasive trees produce large seed crops that easily spread from the areas where they are planted and then choke out or displace native vegetation. Some examples of problematic invasive ornamental trees and shrubs you should avoid are Chinese Tallow, Bradford Pear, Tree-of-Heaven, Chinaberry, and both European and Chinese Privet. If you have these trees or shrubs growing on your property, they should be removed and replaced with native species. Depending on your location and soil, good native trees to consider as replacements include Pecan, Plateau Live Oak (or one of our other native oak species), Cedar Elm, Netleaf Hackberry, Gum Bumelia, Texas Persimmon, and Eve's Necklace. Native Agarita can be used as a hedge to replace Privet, and it provides tasty berries that are excellent for the kitchen as well as for many birds and other animals.

4. Consider participating in a rewilding project. Several key species have been eliminated from all or parts of the Hill Country over the past century, either accidentally or intentionally. Conservation organizations, zoos, the Texas Parks and Wildlife Department, and the U.S. Fish and Wildlife Service are coordinating efforts to bring some of these species back from local extinction. It is important to coordinate any reintroduction efforts with appropriate government agencies, as unauthorized introductions of wildlife are not legal and may be more harmful than beneficial. But careful and planned

re-introductions of some native species are occurring in the Hill Country with landowner permission and the appropriate state and federal permits. Some of these initial efforts appear to be successful, including local reintroductions of Texas Horned Lizards and Black-tailed Prairie Dogs. Almost everyone misses horny toads, and Prairie Dog colonies provide important habitat for many other native species, such as Burrowing Owls. If you are interested in participating in such reintroduction or restoration efforts, contact your local Texas Parks and Wildlife biologist for more information.

5. Watch for and avoid wildlife on roads. Humans and their vehicles are one of the biggest threats to many species of animals in Texas. Snakes, turtles, amphibians, birds, and small mammals are particularly vulnerable to vehicular traffic. These animals are overwhelmingly beneficial to our natural ecosystems and represent an important and beautiful part of what makes the Hill Country special. When animals are abundant on the roads, slow down and save a life or two. Stop, watch, and enjoy the beauty and grace of a Western Coachwhip as it moves like molten metal through the grass on the side of the road. By stopping and watching, you may gain a new appreciation for the animals you encounter along scenic Hill Country roads.

6. Add to public databases on biodiversity. If you enjoy going out to observe and identify native species, why not add your observations to a growing database of information on plants and animals? You can take a photo with your cell phone and post the information and observation to iNaturalist.org or one of several other online databases. Don't worry if you are unsure of the identification; iNaturalist can suggest and assist with identifications, and experts will confirm or correct your suggestions as appropriate. It can be a fun way to participate in understanding the distribution and changes over time of our local plants and animals.

Above all, get out and enjoy our native biodiversity, and keep looking for ways to protect and restore the beauty and diversity of the Hill Country for future generations.

Index

Note: Italicized page numbers indicate material in photographs or illustrations.

acorns, 129–130, 152, 234
aesthetic value of biodiversity, 37
African Clawed Frog, 65
Agarita, 258
agriculture: and bird populations, 176; and the carbon cycle, 164–166; and climate change, 254; and fertilizer use, 166; and grasshopper plagues, 111; and land restoration efforts, 225; and Monarch butterfly populations, 209; value of dung beetles, 104–105
air quality, 179–180
algae, 55–57, 82, 164, 180
alkaline soils, 18
alternative energy sources, 246–247
American Basketflower, 99
American Bison, 118
American Bullfrog, 61, 65
American Goldfinches, 213
American Museum of Natural History, 31
ammonia, 136, 180
ammunition, 240–243
amphibians, 61–62, 63–66, 220–221, 257. *See also* frogs; toads
Annual Bastard Cabbage, 133
annual plants, 222, 231. *See also* grasses and grasslands
Antelope-horns milkweed, 209
antifreeze compounds, 132, 221–222
antlers, 156–158
ants: ecological value of, 170, 186–187; fire ants, 60, 65, 107, 186–189, 238; Harvester Ant, 107–108, 187, 238–239; Texas Leaf-cutter Ant, *186*
aquifers: constant temperatures of, 220; importance to settlers, 69; and insect nests, 186–187; and native grassland restoration, 230; and soils of Edwards Plateau, 19; and underground ecosystems, 73–74; water sources for, 70–71. *See also* water resources
arachnids, *190*, 190–192
architecture of Edwards Plateau, *11*, 13
Argiope aurantia (Yellow Garden Spider), *190*, 190–192
Arizona Cottontop, 94
armadillos, 27–29, 37, *215*, 215–217
Arsesmart, 53
artesian wells, 70
asexual reproduction, 44–46, 52, 56
Ashe Juniper, 17–18, 127, 235
Asian clams, 82–83
Atlantic tropical storms, 22
atmosphere, 65, 164, 255. *See also* climate change; weather
atrazine, 65
Atta texana (Texas Leaf-cutter Ant), *186*
aurochs, 116, 117
Austin Blind Salamander *(Eurycea waterlooensis)*, 32, *73*

bacteria, 25, 31, 35, 36, 56, 75, 136, 164. *See also* cyanobacteria
Balcones Fault Zone, 74
Bald Eagle, 178
barbed wire, 117
Barking Frog, 62, 218
Barton Springs, 32, 69
Basil Beebalm, 99
bats, 75, 147–150, 211
Baylor University, 2, 218
bay systems, 71
bean pods, 137
Bear Spring Formation, 12, *13*
bees, 31, 99
beetles, 125
Bewick's Wrens, 213
Big Bend (region and national park), 2, 245–246
Big Bluestem, 94, 229–230
Big Thicket, 23
Bigtooth Maple, 75, 122
biodiversity: and backyard biology, 169–170; and brush clearing, 233–234; and dung beetles, 104–105; and land restoration efforts, 225–228; and mistletoe, 185; public databases on, 259; and underground ecosystems, 76; value of, 34–38
biological controls, 113, 188
bioluminescence, 78–79
biomedical research, 65
birds: attracting, to gardens, *175*, 175–178; and caterpillars, 196; and cicada emergence, 145; endemic to Hill Country, 31; and grasshopper plagues, 112–113; and mistletoes, 184; and raccoon populations, 160; and seasonal migration, 211–214; and Texas Horned Lizard populations, 239
bison, 42, 92

Black-bellied Whistling-Ducks, 213
blackbirds, 176
Black-chinned Hummingbird, 133, *171*, 171–173, 212, 214
Black Hickory, 18, 122, 216
Blackjack Oak, 18, 123–124, 129
Black-tailed Prairie Dog *(Cynomys ludovicianus)*, 220, *224*, 259
black tourmaline, *8*
Black Walnut, 122
Blanchard's Cricket Frog, 61
Blanco River, 22
Blanco State Park, *3*
blooms, *131*, 131–134, 174, 209
Blotched Watersnake, 141
Bluebird, 177
Bluebonnet, 201
Blue Mistflower, *207*
Blue Mud Plantain, 53
blue topaz, *8*
Bobcat, 108–109, 160
Bobwhite quail, *106*, 160, 177, 188, 213, *233*
bovine spongiform encephalopathy (mad cow disease), 161
Bradford Pear, 258
Brazoria enquistii (Llano Uplift Sandmint), 19, *30*, 32–33
Broad-banded Copperhead, *139*, 140–141
broadleaf weed herbicides, 65
broad-leaved flowering plants (forbs), 92, 227, 234
browse sources, 129–130, 137, 152, 234, 236. *See also* mast sources
brumation, 221
brush control, 233–236
brushlands, 121–122
Bufo punctatus (Red-spotted Toad), 59–60, *205*
bug zappers, 79
Bur Oak, 123–124, 129

Burrowing Owl, 259
burrows, 28, 61–62, 144, 217–218, 227
butterflies, 31, 97–100
button industry, 81

C3 and C4 photosynthesis, 94–95
Cabeza de Vaca, Álvar Núñez, 203–204
cacti, 222, 234, 236
cactus bucks, *155*, 155–158
calcium carbonate, 74, *163*
caliche clay, 17–18
Calliope Hummingbird, 171
Cambrian Explosion, 10, 12
Cambrian stromatolites, 71
Camp Champions, 5
Canada, 208–209, 212
Canadian Columbine, 122
Canary Islands, 116
Canis Major, 144
canoe trips, 85–86
canyons: and aquifers, 70–71; and diverse Hill Country ecology, ix; frog species, 62; and geology of Edwards Plateau, 7; and native grasslands, 91; oak species, 123–124; and the Pecos River, *84*, 85–88; plant species of, *120*; and underground ecosystems, 75; understory plant species, 122
Canyon Wren, 19
captive breeding programs, 239
carbonate minerals, 74, *163*, 165
carbon cycle, 163–166
carbon dioxide, 65, 165, 245–247, 249, 253
carbon footprint, 163–164
Carex genus, 52
Carolina Jointstem, 94
carrying capacity of lands, 154
caterpillars, 193–196, 208

catfishes, 75
cats, 177
cattle: and brush clearing, 234; and brush control measures, 236; and climate change, 254; on Double Helix Ranch, 5; and dung beetles, 102; genetics of Texas cattle, 115–118; and grazing practices, 82, 92, 95, 137, 226, 231, 235–236, 257; and land restoration efforts, 226–227, 229; and mad cow disease, 161; and native grasslands, 92; and soils of Edwards Plateau, 18; and value of biodiversity, 36. *See also* ranches and ranching
caves, 147–150, 220
cayenne pepper sprays, 113
cedar brakes, 18
Cedar Elm, 258
Cedar Waxwing, 184, 213
Celtic culture, 183
cemeteries, 181
Central America, 173
Central Flyway, 53
Central Texas Mineral Region, 75, 152
Charlotte's Web (White), 191
chickadees, 184
Chihuahuan Desert, 23
chill hours, 132–133
Chimney Swift, 212, 214
Chinaberry, 133, 258
Chinese Date *(Ziziphus jujuba)*, 235
Chinese Privet, 258
Chinese Tallow, 133, 258
Chinquapin Oak, 123–124, 129
Chisos Mountains, 245
Christmas Mistletoe *(Phoradendron tomentosum)*, 184–185
chronic wasting disease, 154, 160–162
chytrid fungus, 64

cicadas, *143*, 144–146
Clam Shrimp, 49
clay, *16*, 17–18
Cliff Chirping Frog, 62
Cliff Swallows, 212
climate change: and causes of global warming, 65–66, 165; changes over geologic time, 75; and Cryogenian period, 10; impact on Texas ecosystems, 244–247; and migration patterns, 213; mitigation efforts, 252–255; record cold snaps, *248*; weather vs. climate, 248–251; and wildfires, *244*
climatic adaptations, 203–204
cloning, 78–79
coal, 51, 57, 164, 246
cold tolerance, 132–134
Collared Peccary (javelina), 26–27
Colorado Bend State Park, *3, 163*
Colorado River, 70, 257
Columbus, Christopher, 116
Comal Springs, 69
Common Nighthawk, 212
Common Poorwill, 220
continental drift, 9
Cope, Edward Drinker, 26–27
Cope's Gray Treefrog, 62
Corbicula genus, 82
Couch's Spadefoot, 60–61
COVID-19 pandemic, 64
Cowpen Daisy, 100, 207, 209–210
Coyote, 108–109, 118, 160
Creeping Water Primrose, 53
Crested Caracara, 213, *240*
Cretaceous Period, 14, 74, 85
Creutzfeldt–Jakob disease, 161
Crevice Spiny Lizard, 19
cricket frogs, 61
Crinoid fossils, *13*
crustaceans, 48
crustose lichens, 181

Cryogenian period, 10
cryptorchidism, 156–158
cuckoo bees, 31
cumulonimbus clouds, 24–25
cyanobacteria, 12, 180
Cyclotella cf. *meneghiniana* (diatoms), *55*, 55–57
Cynomys ludovicianus (Black-tailed Prairie Dog), 220, *224*, 259

Dayflower, *97*, 99
DDT, 178
decay and decomposition, 79, 82, 164
deciduous trees, 222
deer: and brush clearing, 233–236; and chronic wasting disease, 154, 160–162; and Hill Country oak trees, 130; and land restoration efforts, 227; management strategies, 159–162; mistletoe as food source, 185; and quail population declines, 108–109; "velvet bucks," *155*, 155–158; and winter adaptations, 216. *See also* Mule Deer; White-tailed Deer
desiccation, 45
development, 64
Devils River, 70, 124, 257
Devil's River State Natural Area, *3*
Devil's Sinkhole State Natural Area, *3*
Devonian Period, *13*
deworming drugs, 103–105
Diamond-backed Watersnake, 141
diapause, 221–222
diatoms *(Cyclotella* cf. *meneghiniana)*, *55*, 55–57
Differential Grasshopper, *110*, 110–112
dioecious plants, 185
direct developer frogs, 62
directional stimuli, 208–209

diseases: and amphibian declines, 64–65; and bats, 149; and cattle breeds, 117; chronic wasting disease, 153–154, 160–162; invasive ants, 187; and lead poisoning, 241; oak wilt disease, 124–126; prion diseases, 160–162

Diverse-leaf Pondweed, 52

Dobie, J. Frank, 117

Dog-Day Cicada, *143*, 144, 146

domestication, 116–117

dormancy, 132–133

Double Helix Ranch: architecture, 13; armadillos at, 29; and climate change, 246, 254; deer populations, 152, 154; described, 5–6; dung beetles, 103–105; Eastern Gamagrass, *168*; endemic Texas species, 31–32; fire ants, 187–188; frogs and toads, 60; and geology of Edwards Plateau, 7, *7*, *8*, 10–11, 13–14; grasshoppers, 113; hailstorms, 194; hummingbirds, 171; hunting, 242; land restoration efforts, 228, 230–231; Lazy Daisies, *90*; location, *3*; migrating species, 213–214; Monarch Butterflies, 207; rainfall amounts, 20–23; Rio Grande Leopard Frogs on, 58; seasonal grasses, 94; snakes, 221; soils of, *16*, 18; solar arrays, *252*; sunrise, *39*; tadpole shrimp, *47*; Texas Longhorn cattle, *115*, 117–118; toads, 205–206; tree blooms, *131*; vernal pools, *40*, 42; wildfires, *244*; wildflowers, *34*; winter weather, *219*

doves, 184

doveweed, 216

dragonflies, 47

drought: and climate change, 246, 251; and grasslands, 92; and Hill Country weather patterns, 20, 22; and Honey Mesquites, 136–137; and native grassland restoration, 230; and oak trees, 124, 128–129; toads' adaptations for, 60

ducks, 214, 216

ducksalad, 54

Ducks Unlimited, 178

duckweed, 52

dung beetles, 101–105, 118

Eastern Bluebird, 177, 184, 213

Eastern Gamagrass, 53, 94, *168*

Eastern Hog-nosed Snake *(Heterodon platirhinos)*, *197*, 197–200, *198*

Eastern Kingbird, 212

Eastern Phoebe, 213

Eastern Treefrog, 122

Eckert James River Bat Cave Preserve, 147–148

economic value of biodiversity, 35–36, 159–162

ecosystems: and bats, 148–149; and climate change, 244; ecological value of ants, 170, 186–187; and land restoration efforts, 228; and snakes, 140, 142; and value of biodiversity, 35–36, 159–162

ectotherms, 217, 220–221

education of author, 2–3

Edwards limestone, 14, 17

Edwards Plateau: aquifers, 70–71; and author's background, ix, xiii–xiv; author's home, 5; Cabeza de Vaca's writings on, 204; climate change, 244; Cope's observations on, 27; deer populations, 151–154, 160; escarpments of, ix, 69–70, 84–85, 123; escarpment waters, 69; fireflies, *77*, 78; freshwater mussels, 82–83; frog species of, 59–60, 62; geology of, 7–15; granitic uplifts, 74; grasshopper

Edwards Plateau (*continued*)
plagues, 112; and Hill Country
endemic species, 31, 33; and Hill
Country weather, 20, 22, 25, 211;
native grasslands, 91–92, 229; oak
species, 123–124; rock art, 89;
scope of, *3*; snakes, 140–141; soils,
16, 16–19; underground ecosystems, 73–76; US Highway 290,
84–85; and value of biodiversity,
37; vernal pools, 41–42; wildflowers, 1, *30*; woodland ecosystems,
121–122
Eggleaf Skullcap, 19
electricity, 251
Electric Shaman (rock art), 87–89, *88*
electric vehicles (EVs), 247, 255
elemental carbon, 165
Ellenburger Group, 12
Ellenburger–San Saba Aquifer, 12
El Niño Southern Oscillation
(ENSO), 21–23
E. naufragia, 33
Enchanted Rock, *3*, 4, 9, 50–51
endemic species, *30*, 31–33, *73*, 76,
121
endocrine cycle, 157
endotherms, 217, 220–221
Enquist, Marshall, 32
environmental toxins, 65, 82
Eocene Epoch, 14, 74, 245–246
erosion, 16–17, 92, 102, 129
Escarpment Cherries, 122
escarpments of Edwards Plateau, ix,
69–70, 84–85, 123
European Privet, 258
European settlers, 12, 69, 91–92,
115, 230
Eurycea (groundwater salamanders),
31–32, *73*
Eurycea tonkawae (Tonkawa Springs
Salamander), 32
Eurycea waterlooensis (Austin Blind
Salamander), 32, *73*

evaporation, 206, 250–251
Eve's Necklace, 258
evolution, 44–45, 83, 121, 204. *See
also* genetics
experimental biology, 79
extinctions, 111

facultative hibernation, 220
Fairy Shrimp, 48
Falcon Cam, 178
feeders, 171, *171*, 174
feral cats, 177
feral cattle, 116–117
feral hogs, 107–109, 130, 254–255
ferns, 51, *120*
finches, 176
fire ants, 60, 65, 107, 186–189, 238
fireflies, 77, 77–80
firewood, 125
fishing, 1–2, 63, 241
flooding, 20, 22, 186–187, 230, 246,
250–251
flowstone, *163*
foliose lichens, 181
food sources: ants as, 187; browse,
129–130, 137, 152, 234, 236; cicadas, 145; grasshoppers, 112, 114;
mast, 152, 234, 236
food waste, 254
forbs: and brush control measures,
234; and deer populations, 152;
and grasshopper plagues, 112; and
land restoration efforts, 227; and
native grasslands, 92; timing of
leaf out and blooming, 133; winter
survival strategies, 222
fossil fuels, 164–166
fossils, 10–15, *13*, 51, 71
Fragrant Mimosa *(Mimosa borealis)*,
233
Fredericksburg, Texas, 4, 27
freeze damage, *131*, 131–132
freshwater bays, 71
Frio City, Texas, 27

Frio River, 2, 70, 257
frogs: and caterpillars, 196; and diatoms, 56; and fire ants, 188; mating choruses, 58–62; population declines, 63–66; and vernal pools, 48. *See also specific species*
fruits, 132–133, 235
frustules, 56
fruticose lichens, 181
fungi: and frog population declines, 64, 65; and lichens, 180; and native grassland restoration, 231–232; oak wilt, 124–126; undiscovered species, 31
fungicides, 126

Gadwalls, 213, 214
gardens, 169–170, 256
Garner State Park, 2, *3*
Gayfeather, 99, 207, 210
geese, 216
gemstones, 8, *8*
genetics: adaptation for cave dwelling, 75–76; and author's background, 4–5; and butterfly migration, 208–209; and cryptorchid bucks, 158; and freshwater mussel lures, 83; and luciferase in fireflies, 78–79; and Periodical Cicadas, 147; and rotifer reproduction, 44–46; and Texas Longhorns, 116–117
geology: and endemic plant life of Hill Country, 32; gemstones of Hill Country, 8, *8*; geological setting of Edwards Plateau, 1, 7, 7–15; and soils, 16–19; and value of biodiversity, 35
Geomys texensis (Llano Pocket Gopher), 19
German settlers, 12, 115
Giant Bald Cypress, 122
Gibson, Fred, 115
glaciers and glaciation, 10, 246, 247

glochidia, 83
glowworms, 78–79
gneiss, 8–9, 157, 179, *179*
Golden-cheeked Warbler, 18
Goldenrod, 210
Gorman Falls, *163*
Government Canyon State Natural Area, *3*
granite, 157, 179
grasses and grasslands: and amphibians, 61, 64; and biodiversity, 36, 91–92; and bird populations, 175–176; and bison wallows, 41; and brush clearing, 234; and carbon dioxide levels, 164–166; and climatic adaptations, 222; at Double Helix Ranch, 6, *168*; and drought, 92; and dung beetles, 103–104; and grasshopper plagues, 112; and Honey Mesquite, 18; invasive species, 96; and land restoration efforts, 225, *229*, 229–232, 258; nonnative species, 92; oak-grassland savannas, 115, 128; pasture grasses, 230; perennial grasses, 118; and seasonal adaptations, *93*, 94–96; and seasonal wetlands, 53; and soils of Edwards Plateau, 92; and Texas Longhorns, 117–118; and water resources, 69; and White-tailed deer, 152. *See also specific species*
grasshoppers, *110*, 110–114
Gray Treefrog *(Hyla chrysoscelis)*, *202*, 221
grazing practices, 82, 92, 95, 137, 226, 231, 235–236, 257. *See also* ranches and ranching
Great American Interchange, 27, 217
Great Depression, 153
Great Plains, 91, 110–111
Great Plains Narrow-mouthed Toad, 61

Great Plains Wildrye, 94
Great Unconformity, 10, 11
Greek culture, 144
greenhouse gases, 165–166, 245, 249
Green Milkweed, 209
Green Toad, 59, 60
Green-winged Teal, 213
Grizzly Bear, 117
groundwater salamanders *(Eurycea)*,
    31
Guadalupe River, 22, 27, 70, 257
Guadalupe River State Park, *3*
guano, 75
Gulf Coast Toad, 59, 60
Gulf of Mexico, 22, 212
Gum Bumelia, 122, 258

Habitat for Humanity, 247
habitat loss, 64, 78, 107, 169–170,
    176
habitat restoration, 109
hail, 23–25, 193–194
hairstreak butterflies, 185
Harvester Ant, 107–108, 187,
    238–239
haustorium, 184
hawks, 148, 235
hazardous material disposal, 257
Heller's Rosettegrass, 94
hemiparasitics, 184
herbicides, 65–66, 137–138, 226
hermaphroditism, 49
Heterodon platirhinos (Eastern
    Hog-nosed Snake), *197*, 197–
    200, *198*
hibernation, 220–221
Hickory Aquifer, 12
Hickory Sandstone, 10–12, *11*, *167*
Highland Lakes, 5
Hill Country State Natural Area, *3*
Hillis, David M.: acquisition of
    Double Helix Ranch, xiii–xv, 7;
    background and education, xiii–xv

Hillis, Erec, xiv, 5, 7, 11
Hillis, Jonathan, xiv, 5, 7, 11
Hispaniola, island of, 116
hog-nosed snakes, *197*, 197–200,
    198
Holcopasites jerryrozeni (Rozen's
    Cuckoo Bee), 31
Honey Creek State Natural Area, *3*
Honey Mesquite, 18, *135*, 135–138,
    185, 235–236
hormones, 65, 132–133, 157
Horsetails, 51, 52
Houston, Texas, 179, 245
hummingbirds, 97–100, *171*,
    171–174, 212, 214
hunting: and deer population,
    153–154, 159–162; and land
    restoration efforts, 225–228; and
    lead poisoning, 240–243; and
    quail population, 108; and value of
    biodiversity, 35–37; and waterfowl
    habitat, 178
hurricanes, 22
hydrology, 35. *See also* water
    resources
Hyla chrysoscelis (Gray Treefrog),
    202, 221

Iberian Peninsula, 116
igneous rocks, 19
iNaturalist.org, 259
Independence Creek, 70, *77*, 85
Indiangrass, 94, 229, *229*
Industrial Revolution, 164–165
Inks Lake State Park, *3*
inorganic compounds, 165–166
insecticides: and backyard biology,
    170; and bat populations, 149; and
    bird population declines, 177–
    178; and dung beetles, 103–105;
    and fireflies, 79–80; and grasshop-
    per plagues, 113–114; and land
    restoration efforts, 226; and quail

population declines, 109; and Texas Horned Lizard populations, 238–239

insects: and backyard biology, 170; and bat predation, 148–149; and bird population, 176–177; and grasslands, 92; and seasonal migration, 211–213; undiscovered species, 31; and winter survival strategies, 221, 222. *See also specific types and species*

Interstate 10, 84

invasive species: and brush control measures, 235–236; fire ants, 60, 65, 107, 186–189, 238; grasses, 96; and restoration efforts, 257–258; and timing of leaf out and blooming, 133; weeds, 230

iron pyrite, *8*

Irving, Washington, 184

ivermectin, 103–105

jaguars, 27

James River, 71

James River Bat Cave, 147

Japanese Brome, 96

javelina (Collared Peccary), 26–27

Johnsongrass, 133

Jujube, 235

junipers, 121, 123. *See also* Ashe Juniper

keystone species, 185, 227

Kickapoo Cavern State Park, *3*

King Ranch Bluestem, 133

Lacey Oaks, 18, 123, 129

Lake Amistad, 86

land stewardship ethic, 36

La Niña, 21–23, 59

La Relación de Álvar Núñez Cabeza de Vaca (Cabeza de Vaca), 204

larks, 176

Laurentia, 8–10

Lazy Daisies, *90*

lead, 178–179, *240*, 240–243

Lee, Robin, 63–64

legal battles over water, 70

Lemon Mint, 99

leopard frogs, 56. *See also* Rio Grande Leopard Frog

Leopold, Aldo, xiii

Lewis Canyon, 84, *87*

lichens, 170, *179*, 179–182

lightning bugs, *77*, 77–80

light pollution, 78–79, 176

limestone: and brush control measures, 235; and the carbon cycle, 165; and geology of Edwards Plateau, 12, 14; and oak trees, 123, 129; and the Pecos River, 85; and soils of Edwards Plateau, 19; and underground ecosystems, 74

Little Bluestem, 94, 229

Little Walnuts, 122

Live Oak, 124, 128–129

Live Oak Creek, 84

livestock, 52, 185, 234, 236. *See also* cattle; ranches and ranching

lizards, 177, 196, 217, 221. *See also* Texas Horned Lizard *(Phrynosoma cornutum)*

Llano Pocket Gopher *(Geomys texensis)*, 19

Llano River: and aquifers, 71; freshwater mussels, 81–83; and geology of Edwards Plateau, 12–14; and Hill Country weather patterns, 22; and restoration of native species, 257; and value of biodiversity, 37

Llano Uplift: and author's background, 4–5; and deer populations, 152, 153–154, 156–157; and geology of Edwards Plateau, 9, 12; lichen growth, *179*; lichens of,

Llano Uplift (*continued*)
179, *179*; location, *3*; and soils of
Edwards Plateau, 17, 18–19; and
underground ecosystems, 75
Llano Uplift Sandmint *(Brazoria
enquistii)*, 19, *30*, 32–33
loams, *16*, 17
logging, 209
Longhorn Cavern State Park, *3*
Longhorns, 5, *115*, 116–118
Lost Maples State Natural Area, *3*,
75
Lotebush *(Ziziphus obtusifolia)*,
234–235
lovegrasses, 94
Lower Pecos River, 84–89, *87*
luciferase, 78–79
Lyndon B. Johnson State Park, *3*

mad cow disease, 161
Madrones, 122
Mallard, 213
Maltese Star Thistle, 133
mammals, 31, 137, 145, 220, 239
mammiferous cluds, *223*
mammoths, 137
Mariposa Monarca Biosphere
Reserve, 209
Mason, Texas, *11*, 249
Mason County, Texas, 147, 231
Mason Mountain Wildlife Manage-
ment Area, 239
mast sources, 152, 234, 236. *See also*
browse sources
mating calls, 58–62, 144–146
McTavish, Emily Jane, 116
meadows, *90*, *119*
medicinal compounds, 181
Medina River, 27, 70, 257
megafauna, 13
Melanoplus spretus (Rocky Mountain
Locust), 110–114
mesopredators, 107

Mesquite Looper, *193*, 194–195
mesquite trees, 137, 194, 236. *See
also* Honey Mesquite
metabolism, 164, 212, 219–222
metamorphic rocks, 19
metamorphosis, 79
methane, 165
Mexican Axolotl, 65
Mexican Free-tailed Bat, *147*, 148,
211–212
Mexican Plum, *131*
Mexican White Oak, 123–124
Mexico, 173, 208–209
Michoacán, Mexico, 207–208
microscopic animals: algae, 55–57,
82, 164, 180; diatoms, *55*, 55–57;
rotifers, *43*, 43–46
microsporidia, 113
migration: bird species, 176; and
Great American Interchange, 27;
hummingbirds, 173; Monarch
Butterflies, 208–210; wildfowl, 53;
as winter survival, 211–214
milkweeds, 208–209
Mimosa borealis (Fragrant Mimosa),
233
mints, 99
Miocene, 74–75
Mississippian Age, 13
Mississippi Kite, 212
Mistletoe, 152, *183*, 183–185
molds, 174
Monarch Butterflies, 100, *207*,
207–210, 214
Monarda genus, 99
Moors, 116
mosquitoes, 48, 79
moths, 99, 195–196
Mountain Lion, 27, 109, 117–118,
160
Mule Deer, 161, 162
Muller, Hermann J., 45
Muller's Ratchet, 45

mussels, 81–83

Mustang Grapes, 152

mutations, 44–46, 76. *See also* genetics

mutualistic relationships, 61, 231

naming of new species, 32–33

nanotechnology, 57

Native American Seed, 258

natural gas, 164, 245–246

natural selection, 75–76, 83, 117. *See also* genetics

The Nature Conservancy, 148, *256*

Nearctic migratory species, 212

nectar, 97–99, 174, 209

Neff, Jack, 31

nematodes, 31

Neotropic migratory species, 212

nesting birds, 177, 194–196, 214

nests, 172, 214, 217–218

Netleaf Hackberry, 122, 152, 258

Nine-banded Armadillo, 26, 28–29, *215*, 215–217

nitidulids, 125

nitrates, 179

nitrogen fixation, 138

Nobel Prize, 45

nonnative species, 92, 95–96, 133, 226, 257, 259. *See also* invasive species

Norse culture, 183

North American Monarch Conservation Plan, 209

Northern Bobwhite, 99, 107

Northern Harrier, 213

Northern Polar Vortex, 250

Nosema locustae (NoLo), 113

Nueces River, 27, 70, 257

Oak Leafroller, 193–195

oak trees: acorns, 129–130, 152, 234; and cicadas, 145; and cold snaps, *248*; and deer populations, 160;

and fall colors, *127*; and Hickory Sandstone hills, *167*; and Hill Country adaptations, 127–130; and Hill Country weather patterns, 22–23; and land restoration efforts, 229; and lichen growth, 179; oak-grassland savannas, 115, 122; oak leaf camouflage, 141; oak wilt disease, 123–126; and soil quality, 129; and water resources, 129; and winter food sources, 216; and woodlands ecosystems, 121. *See also specific species*

obligatory hibernation, 220

ocean levels, 245

Ocelot, 27

oil, 57, 164, 245–246

Old Tunnel State Park, *3*

Old Yeller (Gibson), 115

Oligocene, 74

"On the Zoological Position of Texas" (Cope), 26–27

Ordovician limestones, 12

organic carbon, 164

Ornate Box Turtle, 106

overgrazing, 82, 92, 95, 137, 226, 231, 235–236, 257

overwintering grounds, 209

owls, 148

Oxford English Dictionary, 53

oxygen, 55–56

Oyamel Fir forest, 209

Pacific Jet Stream, 21

Pacific Ocean, 21

Painted Bunting, *175*, 212, 214

Palmetto, 122

Panamanian Isthmus, 27, 217

Pandale, Texas, 85–86

pandemics, 64

parasites: as biological control of pests, 113, 194–196; and fire ant controls, 108, 188; and oak wilt

parasites (*continued*)
disease, 124–126; and quail population declines, 108; and Texas Horned Lizard populations, 239
pasture grasses, 230
peach trees, 132
Pecan, 122, 152, 216, 258
Pecos River, 70, 84–89, *87*, 257
Pecos Valley, 85
Pedernales Falls State Park, *3*, 5
Pedernales River, *68*, 257
Pennsylvanian Age, 13
pepper sprays, 113
Peregrine Falcon, 178
perennial grasses, 94, 118, 222
Periodic Cicada, 145–146
pesticides, 60, 66, 107, 196
petroleum reserves, 57
pet trade, 65
pharmaceuticals, 33
Phoradendron tomentosum (Christmas Mistletoe), 184–185
phorid flies, 108, 188
Photinus genera, 78
photoperiod, 133, 156
photosynthesis: and the carbon cycle, 164; and coastal Laurentia, 9; and diatoms, *55*, 55–57; and Hill Country oak trees, 128; and lichens, 180; and native grassland restoration, 231; and seasonal grasses, 94–95; and underground ecosystems, 75; and value of biodiversity, 35
Photuris genera, 78
Phrynosoma cornutum (Texas Horned Lizard), 37, 106–107, 187, 237–239, 259
phytoestrogens, 157
phytoplankton, 57
pigs, 130. *See also* feral hogs
Pillwort, 51
Pintail, 213

pioneer organisms, 181
plagues, 110–114. *See also* pandemics
Plateau Live Oak *(Quercus fusiformis)*, 123–124, *127*, 128, 152, 258
plate tectonics, 9
Pleistocene Epoch, 15, 71, 137
Pliocene Epoch, 74
Poa arachnifera (Texas Bluegrass), *93*, 94–95
pocket-prairie, 256–258
poison ivy, 160
poisons, 149, 188, 238–239. *See also* lead
polar ice caps, 165, 250
Polar Vortex, 250
pollination and pollinators: amphibians, 65; and bird population declines, 177; and flower structures, 97–100; and timing of leaf out and blooming, 133
pomegranates, 133
pondweeds, 52
Portuguese colonists, 116
Post Oak, 18, 123, 129, 193–194
prairie dogs. *See* Black-tailed Prairie Dog; White-tailed Prairie Dog
Precambrian era, 10
precipitation, 251
predators and predation: and armadillo defenses, 29; and bat populations, 148–149; chemical deterrents, 208; and cicada emergence, 145–146; and deer populations, 152–153, 160; and ecosystem health, 35; and fireflies, 78–79; and freshwater mussels, 82–83; and hognose snakes, 199; and Horned Lizards, 238–239; and Longhorn cattle evolution, 116–118; Lotebush as protection from, 235; and mutualistic relationships, 61; and quail

population declines, 107–109; and rodent population, 140; and side effects of pest controls, 113–114, 177; and spider web designs, 191–192; and Texas Longhorns, 117–118; and underground ecosystems, 75; and vernal pools, 42, 47, 49, 66, 257

Prickly Pear, 152, 234, 236

prion diseases, 160–162

Project Drawdown, 253

public transportation, 255

"puffing adders." *See* Eastern Hog-nosed Snake *(Heterodon platirhinos)*

Puma, 153

Purple Martin, 212

purpose of text, xiii–xiv, 6

quail, 106–109, 112–113, 160, 213, 233–235

Quercus fusiformis (Plateau Live Oak), 123–124, *127*, 128, 152, 258

quillworts, 51–52

raccoons, 66, 107–109, 160, 239

radiation, 45

rainfall: and brush control measures, 234; and climate change, 246, 250–251; and dung beetles, 102; and Hill Country weather patterns, 20–23; and native grasslands, 92, 230; rainwater collection, 6; and seasonal grasses, 94; and soils of Llano Uplift, 17; and value of biodiversity, 36

rainfrogs, 122

ranavirus, 64–65

ranches and ranching: and bird populations, 176; and brush clearing, 234–236; and dung beetles, 103; and grazing practices, 82, 92, 95, 137, 226, 231, 235–236, 257; and

land restoration efforts, 225–232, 256; and mesquite regrowth, 137; and pocket-prairie restoration, 256–258; and quail population declines, 109; and value of biodiversity, 35–36

rangelands, 36, 103, 254

raptors, 178

rattlesnakes, 140–141

recreation, 225–228, 257

Red Imported Fire Ants *(Solenopsis invicta)*, 187–188

red oaks, 124

Red River, 145

Red-spotted Toad *(Bufo punctatus)*, 59–60, *205*

refugee crises, 245

regrowth mesquite, 137

Remedy herbicide, 137–138

reproductive diapause, 208

reptiles, 220–221

Rescuegrass, 96

restoration efforts, 225–228

resurrection plants, 157

Ringtails, 19

Rio Grande Leopard Frog, 58, 61, *63*

riparian habitat, 66, 80, 257

rivers, 22

rock art, 85–89, *86*, *87*, *88*

Rocky Mountain Locust *(Melanoplus spretus)*, 110–114

Rocky Mountains, 121

rodents, 92, 140

Rodinia, 9–10

roller dung beetles, 102

roots, 145, 222, 230

rotational grazing, 118, 236

rotifers, *43*, 43–46

Rozen's Cuckoo Bee *(Holcopasites jerryrozeni)*, 31

Ruby-throated Hummingbirds, 171–173

Rufous Hummingbirds, 171
rushes, 52

salamanders, 32–33, 75–76
San Antonio, Texas, 1, 2, 27
San Antonio Springs and River,
  69–70
sandalwood, 184
sand and sandy soils, *16*, 17
A Sand County Almanac (Leopold),
  xiii
Sand Dropseed, 94
Sandhill Crane, 37, 214
sandstones, 10–12, *11*, 51, *167*
sandy soils, 235
San Felipe Springs, 69
San Fernando Academy, 201
San Marcos Springs, 69
San Saba County, 51
San Saba River, 12
Santales order, 184
Saturnalia, 183
savannas, 127
Scissor-tailed Flycatchers, 212
Scouring Rushes, 52
screwworms, 153
sea levels, 245–246
Seaquist House, *11*
seasons: and blooming plants, *131*,
  131–134; and cicada emergence,
  144; seasonal pools and wetlands,
  47–48, *63*, 64, 66, *67*, 257; winter
  freezes, *131*, 221. *See also* climate
  change; weather
sedges, 52
sedimentary rocks, 16, 74. *See also*
  limestone; sandstone
seeds, 187, 231
selection pressures, 75–76
Seminole Canyon State Park, *3*
settlers, 12, 69, 91–92, 115, 230
sexual reproduction, 44–46, 56
shales, 14

Shin Oak, 18, 129
shrubs, *233*
Sideoats Grama, 94
Sierra Madre Oriental, 121
silky-flycatchers, 184
silt, *16*, 17
Silver Bluestem, 94
Sirius, 144
Six-Weeks Fescue, 94
The Sketch Book (Irving), 184
skunks, 1–2
Smartweed, 53
Smithsonian Institution, 26
smokey quartz, *8*
snakebites, 142
snakes, 36, *139*, 139–142, 145, 148,
  221
snow, *20*
Snowball Earth (Cryogenian
  period), 10
soils: and ants, 186–187; and brush
  control measures, 235; and the
  carbon cycle, 165; at Double Helix
  Ranch, *16*; and dung beetles, 102,
  104; and grasslands, 92; and hunting ammunition, 242; of Llano
  Uplift, 16–19; and oak trees, 129
solar power, 5, 246–247, *252*,
  253–254
Solenopsis invicta (Red Imported
  Fire Ants), 187–188
South American Fire Ants, 107
South Llano River State Park, *3*
Spadefoot toads, 60–61
Spanish colonists, 116
Spanish Oak, 123–124, *127*
sparrows, 176
Sparta Sand Formation, 14
Speargrass (Texas Wintergrass), 94
spiders, *190*, 190–192
spikemosses, 51, 157
spore-bearing plants, 51–52
Spotted Beebalm, 99

Spotted Chorus Frog, 59
springs, 69, 74
stabilimentum, *190*, 191
Standing Cypress, *97*, 99, 174
star sapphire, *8*
stewardship ethic, 36
stock tanks, 42
Stockton Plateau, 85
stomata, 128
streams, 22
Strecker, John K., 4, 218
Strecker's Chorus Frog, 59, 217–218
stromatolites, 71
subsistence hunting, 153
Sugar Maples, 122
sunflowers, 216
Switchgrass, 94, 229
symbiosis, 180

tadpoles, 48, 56
Tadpole Shrimp, *47*, 48–49
tallgrasses, 36, 229–231
tallow, 117
tarsiers, 245
Teloschistes exilis, 181
temperatures, 21–25, 131–134, 245,
    248–251. *See also* climate change;
    weather
termites, 238
testosterone, 156
Texas Bluebonnet, 99
Texas Bluegrass *(Poa arachnifera)*,
    93, 94–95
Texas Capitol Building, 9
Texas Coralsnake, 141
Texas Fatmucket, 82–83
Texas Fawnsfoot, 82
Texas Heelsplitter, 82
Texas Horned Lizard *(Phrynosoma
    cornutum)*, 37, 106–107, 187,
    237–239, 259
Texas Leaf-cutter Ant *(Atta texana)*,
    186

Texas Longhorn cattle, 5, 115–118
Texas Nature Conservancy, *256*
Texas Parks and Wildlife Depart-
    ment, 152, 162, 227, 258–259
Texas Patch-nosed Snake, 221
Texas Persimmon, 152, 216, 234,
    236, 258
Texas Pimpleback, 82
Texas Prickly Pear, 216
Texas Red Oak, 18, 129
Texas State Amphibian, 59
Texas Toad, 59, 60
Texas Wintergrass (Speargrass),
    94–95
thrushes, 184
thunderstorms, 24–25, *223*
toads, 48, 122, 188, *205*, 205–206
tourism, 35, 37, 71
Town Mountain Granite, 9
Trans-Pecos region, 84–85
transpiration, 128
trapping, 108
tree bark, 181
Tree-of-Heaven, 133, 258
Triangle Pigtoe, 82
Trinity limestones, 14, 17
Triops genus, 48
troglobites, 76
tropical frogs, 62
tropical rainforests, 64
tropics, 25
tubular flowers, 174
tumblebugs, 102
tunneler dung beetles, 102
turkeys, 112, 160, 213
turtles, 217

ultraviolet light, 99, 191
underground burrows, 220–221
undiscovered species, 31
unionids, 81
United States, 209
University of Kansas, 4

University of Miami, 4
University of Texas: and author's
    background, 4–5; Biodiver-
    sity Center, xiii–xv, 5, 32, 178,
    195; Center for Computational
    Biology and Bioinformatics, 5;
    and fire ant controls, 108, 188;
    Peregrine Falcon nests, 178; and
    rotifer research, 45; School of
    Biological Sciences, 5
U.S. Fish and Wildlife Service, 258
U.S. Highway 290, 84–86

Valley Springs Gneiss, 8, 10, 19, 32,
    167
vascular plants, 51
venomous snakes, 140
Veracruz, Mexico, 116
vernal pools: crustaceans of, *47*,
    47–49; on Double Helix Ranch,
    40; flora of, *50*, 50–54; forms
    of, 41–42; and frog population
    declines, 66; and Rio Grande
    Leopard Frogs, *63*; rocky pools, *67*
vireos, 212
viruses, 64

warblers, 176, 212
wasps, 195
waste disposal, 257
Waterclover, 51
waterfowl, 52, 177–178, 213,
    241–242
water hyacinths, 53
water resources: artesian wells, 70;
    and backyard biology, 169; compe-
    tition for, 70, 129; at Double Helix
    Ranch, *168*; and dung beetles,
    102; and freshwater mussels, 81;
    and Hill Country oak trees, 128;
    and land restoration efforts, 227;
    and lead poisoning, 241; rotifers,
    43, 43–46; and value of ant nests,

186–187; and the water cycle,
    250–251; water holes, *106*; water-
    ways, 257. *See also* drought; rainfall
weather: and caterpillars, 193–196;
    climatic adaptations, 203–204,
    215–218, 219–222; freeze dam-
    age, *131*, 131–132; and grass-
    hopper plagues, 112; and Hill
    Country weather patterns, 20–25;
    and hummingbird metabolism,
    174; snowstorms, *20*. *See also*
    climate change; rainfall
webs, *190*, 190–192
wells, 70
Western Coachwhip, 259
Western Cottonmouth, 141
Western Diamond-backed Rattle-
    snake, 140
wetlands, 79, 257
White, E. B., 191
white oaks, 124
White Pelican, *211*
White Shin Oak, 123
White-tailed Deer, 108–109,
    151–153, *155*, 155–158, *159*, 234
White-tailed Prairie Dog, 220
White-winged Dove, 213
Whorled Milkweed, 209
Wilberns Formation, 12
wild cattle, 115
wildfires, 18, 235, *244*
wildflowers, *34*, 37, 80, *119*, 128
wildlife management, 108–109,
    152–154, 233
Wild Turkey, 160, 177–178
wind energy, 253
Winter Ryegrass, 96
winter weather: cold fronts, 193,
    211; and migration, 211–214;
    physiological adaptations,
    215–218, 219–222; winter freezes,
    131, 221
Wisconsin, 124

wolves, 117, 153

Woodhouse's Toad, 59, 60

Writing Spider *(Argiope aurantia)*, *190*, 190–192

Wyoming, 161

Yaupon, 152

Yellow-billed Cuckoo, 212

Yellow Garden Spider *(Argiope aurantia)*, *190*, 190–192

Yellow Stonecrop, 210

Yucatán Peninsula, 212

Zesch, Butch, 34–35, 38, 231

Zesch, Hal, 34–35, 38

Zesch Ranch, 36

Zig-Zag (Zipper) Spider *(Argiope aurantia)*, *190*, 190–192

Ziziphus jujuba (Chinese Date of Asia), 235

Ziziphus obtusifolia (Lotebush), 234–235

Zizotes Milkweed, 209

zoos, 239

zygotes, 56